*"There is one thing I would be glad to ask you.
When a mathematician engaged in investigating
physical actions and results has arrived
at his own conclusions, may they not be expressed
in common language as fully, clearly, and
definitely as in mathematical formulae? If so,
would it not be a great boon to such as we
to express them so—translating them out of
their hieroglyphics that we also might
work upon them by experiment."*

Letter from Michael Faraday to Clerk Maxwell, reprinted in *Atomic
Spectra*, by A. C. Candler (London: Cambridge University Press, 1937).

**Fig. 1.** Ground level.

**Fig. 2.** One quantum.

**Fig. 3.** Large J.

**Fig. 4.** Transition moment.

**Fig. 5.** Forbidden transition.

**Fig. 6.** Excited state.

**H. BRIAN DUNFORD,** *University of Alberta*

# ELEMENTS OF DIATOMIC
# MOLECULAR SPECTRA

**ADDISON-WESLEY PUBLISHING COMPANY**
*Reading, Massachusetts · Menlo Park, California · London · Don Mills, Ontario*

This book is in the
**Addison-Wesley Series in Chemistry**

*Consulting Editor*
FRANCIS T. BONNER

# PREFACE

This textbook on spectroscopy is designed for use in physical chemistry courses, and, in particular, for the introductory physical chemistry course. Few texts in physical chemistry contain more than the briefest discussion of rotation and vibration-rotation spectra of diatomic molecules. For the latter, the approximation is usually made that the spectrum consists of a series of equispaced lines. A precise treatment of vibration-rotation spectra, as well as the simpler electronic spectra requires nothing more complex than the use of the equation for a parabola, and the analysis of the most complex electronic spectra involves a study of deviations from parabolic equations. No knowledge of mathematics beyond an introduction to calculus is required, and most of the problems in this text can be solved with simple arithmetic.

A study of spectroscopic data fixes a picture in the student's mind of how energy can be absorbed by matter, a picture sadly lacking in classical thermodynamics. It establishes the concept of energy levels and quantization of energy, and thus provides an excellent *preparation* for the study of statistical and quantum mechanics. It provides experimental evidence for many of the features of atomic and molecular orbital theory. Finally, it enables the student to learn how fundamental molecular constants are obtained, which in itself is a worth-while endeavor.

Some arbitrary choices of material were necessary for a volume of this size. The presentation of experimental evidence has been used to justify the conclusions, wherever possible. A few simplifying assumptions have been made; for example, it is assumed that multiplet Π- and Δ-states adhere strictly to Hund's case (a). Study from the present text should, we hope, facilitate use by undergraduate chemists of the standard reference in the field, *Spectra of Diatomic Molecules*, 2nd ed., by G. Herzberg (Princeton, N.J.: Van Nostrand, 1950).

I am personally indebted for the influence of two excellent teachers: Dr. Alex Douglas, of the Pure Physics Division, National Research Council, Ottawa, and Dr. John Callomon, University College, University of London. I would also like to acknowledge the helpful comments by my colleagues Drs. Fraser Birss, Serafin Fraga, Harry Habgood, Walter Harris, and Mr. Richard Messmer, and particularly by Dr. Francis T. Bonner of the State University of New York at Stony Brook and Dr. Robin Hochstrasser of the University of Pennsylvania, who critically reviewed the entire manuscript; also the assistance of Mr. Donald Whalen, who checked the problems, and Mrs. Barbara Roth, who typed the manuscript. I thank Dr. Keith Innes of Vanderbilt University, who is responsible for bringing to my attention the cartoon used in the frontispiece, Dr. Henry Bent of the University of Minnesota, who dubbed in the captions, and Mr. Harry Lyons for his excellent artistry. I hold myself personally responsible for any shortcomings or errors in this volume, and I would sincerely appreciate your comments. I now know why many authors thank their wives for their patience and understanding, Dee, and I do the same.

*Edmonton, Canada*                                         H.B.D.
*September 1967*

# CONTENTS

## CHAPTER 1

# INTRODUCTION

### PARTICLES AND WAVES; MATTER AND ENERGY

A prime requisite for an understanding of the behavior of atoms and molecules, and of spectroscopic observations, is a knowledge of the dual nature of particles and waves.

Newton postulated a corpuscular theory as to the nature of light in the latter part of the 17th century, about the same time that Huygens postulated his wave theory. The stature of Newton was such that his theory was dominant until the 19th century, when further experimental work, notably by Young, appeared to put the wave theory on an unshakeable foundation. The wave theory was further strengthened by the theoretical work of Maxwell, so that towards the end of the 19th century, the view was widely held by physicists that little more remained to be learned about electromagnetic radiation, of which visible light forms one component. The theory of electromagnetic radiation was developed to such a degree of refinement that it could be used to predict the distribution of wavelengths of light emitted by a blackbody radiator. The latter, by definition, is a body which is a perfect absorber of incident radiation, and conversely is a perfect emitter of radiation resulting from its own thermal energy. This means that its incident and emitted radiation are of the same wavelength distribution. In other words, a blackbody is in equilibrium with the observed radiation. A blackbody radiator can be approximated experimentally by many solids, particularly if they are shaped in the form of a cavity with a small orifice, so that the percentage of radiation which escapes is so small that thermal equilibrium is always maintained. The observed change in color of an incandescent solid from red to white with increased temperature illustrates qualitatively a property of a radiator—namely that the average energy of its emitted radiation is shifted to shorter wavelengths, or higher frequencies, with increased temperature. Classical theory, based on the equipartition of energy principle, predicted that at *any given temperature*, the intensity of emitted radiation would increase with increasing frequency. The experimental result, obtained by use of an apparatus similar to that shown schematically in Fig. 1–1, was that the intensity of emitted light at any given temperature always passed through a maximum as a function of increasing frequency. This result, viewed with abject horror, was dubbed the "ultraviolet catastrophe" by physicists

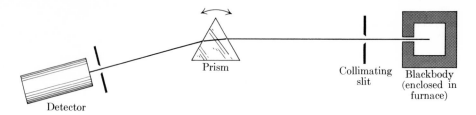

**Fig. 1-1.** Schematic diagram of an apparatus used to measure intensity distribution of a blackbody radiator as a function of wavelength.

of the time. The experimental observations were finally rationalized by Planck, who concluded that individual oscillators exist, the energy of each of which is given by $E = h\nu$. Planck's constant, $h$, has units of energy $\times$ time. The frequency of oscillation, $\nu$, has units of time$^{-1}$.

A famous extension to Planck's relation has been made by Einstein:

$$E = h\nu = mc^2. \tag{1-1}$$

This equation extends the dual concept from light to matter. Just as Planck showed that it was necessary to postulate that light has particle as well as wave properties, Einstein showed that, in principle, matter and energy are interconvertible. The conversion of matter into energy is rapidly becoming a routine matter, through nuclear fission or nuclear fusion reactions.*

Our interest in Eq. (1-1) is twofold. First, it enables one to calculate the *effective* mass possessed by a light quantum. Second, and more important for our purposes, a valuable extension to Eq. (1-1) was made by de Broglie, who postulated that it is possible to substitute $v$, the velocity of a real particle in the classical sense, for $c$, the velocity of light. Thus

$$h\nu = mv^2. \tag{1-2}$$

This equation implies that all particles, when moving, have wave motion associated with them. The present-day interpretation states that for a moving particle, for example an electron, there is an associated wave packet, as illustrated in Fig. 1-2. This places an uncertainty on both the position and momentum of the electron, since the exact location of the electron at any given time is uncertain. Heisenberg expressed this uncertainty as

$$\Delta p \Delta x \geq h/4\pi, \tag{1-3}$$

where $\Delta p$ is the uncertainty in momentum and $\Delta x$ is the uncertainty in position. Thus, if the position of the electron could be defined exactly, the momentum would be completely uncertain, whereas if the velocity is known

---

* May mankind acquire the restraints rapidly enough to keep these reactions controlled!

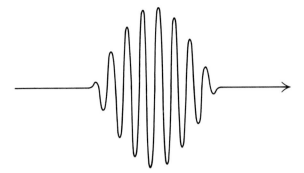

**Fig. 1–2.** The concept of a wave packet associated with a moving particle, for example, an electron.

exactly, then the position becomes completely uncertain. This uncertainty relation, which is a cause for puzzlement, is also the source of the greatest strength of modern quantum and wave-mechanical theory. In principle, scientists recognized at least three centuries ago that there is no point in asking questions which cannot be answered, a point of view generally accepted by philosophers in the 20th century. Where the classical physicists erred, and where Bohr was in error with his introductory quantum theory of atoms, was that they tried to be more precise than nature will allow. The dual nature of particles and waves places a restriction on the precision of experiment. If one attempts to locate an electron precisely, one must use a sensitive probe. However, the finest probe that any scientist can devise will cause disturbance in the system, so that the original position of the electron is changed.

It is now universally accepted that the dual nature of particles and waves is correct. Particularly lucid experiments which proved the wave nature of particles and the converse, were the diffraction experiments of Davisson and Germer, who showed that a beam of electrons is diffracted by a crystal grating, as is a beam of x-rays; and the famous photoelectric experiment, which could only be explained on the basis that light has quantum or particle properties. The photoelectric effect is the term used to describe the bombardment of a metal surface with monochromatic light, which results in electron emission. When the energy of emitted electrons is measured as a function of frequency of the light, results as summarized in Fig. 1–3 are obtained. Until a certain frequency of radiation, characteristic of the metal, is reached, no electrons are emitted. Then, at a critical frequency, electrons are emitted instantly. Both of these observations contradict the behavior predicted by wave theory. The energy of the emitted electrons is a linear function of frequency of the incident radiation. This can be expressed as

$$E = h\nu - h\nu_0$$
$$= h\nu - w,$$

$$(1\text{–}4)$$

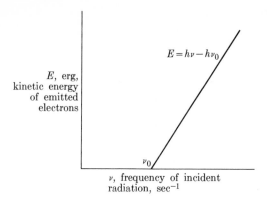

$$E = h\nu - h\nu_0$$

$E$, erg, kinetic energy of emitted electrons

$\nu_0$

$\nu$, frequency of incident radiation, $\sec^{-1}$

**Fig. 1–3.** A plot of photoelectric effect results, the slope of which is equal to Planck's constant, $h$.

where $\nu_0$ is the characteristic frequency at which electron emission begins. The term $h\nu_0$ is often called the work function of the metal, $w$. Thus from a plot of $E$ vs. $\nu$, the value of Planck's constant is obtained directly from the slope.

It is therefore clear that one can observe particle or wave properties of either light or matter by the appropriate choice of experiment. We are now in a much better position to understand spectroscopic observations on the behavior of molecules.

## UNITS

The frequency $\nu$ is usually expressed in $\sec^{-1}$. In order to express $\nu$ in other forms, use is made of the velocity of propagation of electromagnetic radiation, namely $c = 3 \times 10^{10}$ cm/sec. Thus $\nu/c$, defined as $\bar{\nu}$, has the units of $\text{cm}^{-1}$, which are commonly called *wave-number* units. Inversely, $c/\nu = \lambda$ is called the *wavelength* and has units of cm. The wavelength can also be expressed in Angstrom units, Å, obtained from the relation 1 cm $= 10^8$ Å; in millimicrons, m$\mu$, given by 1 cm $= 10^7$ m$\mu$; or microns, $\mu$, given by 1 cm $= 10^4 \mu$. To convert $\nu$ to energy in erg/molecule, or more generally erg/particle, multiply by Planck's constant, $h = 6.62 \times 10^{-27}$ erg-sec. For example, a frequency $\nu$ of $10^{12}$ $\sec^{-1}$ multiplied by $h$ yields $6.62 \times 10^{-15}$ erg per particle of particular interest, whether it be a molecule, an electron, or a photon. The conversion of erg/molecule to cal/mole requires two factors; one is the mechanical equivalent of heat, 1 cal $= 4.186 \times 10^7$ erg; and the other is Avogadro's number, $N = 6.023 \times 10^{23}$ molecules per mole. Finally, the units of electron volts should be explained. If a single electron is subjected to the acceleration in a field of one volt potential, it has one electron volt of energy. The relationship between electrical and kinetic energy is given by

$$Ve = \tfrac{1}{2}mv^2. \qquad (1\text{–}5)$$

Since $V = 1$ volt, and $e$, the charge on the electron is $1.6 \times 10^{-19}$ coulombs, the product is $1.6 \times 10^{-19}$ in units of volt-coulombs or joules. Thus the interconversion of energy units involving molecules, sub-atomic particles such as electrons, and photons is readily carried out. Chemists are familiar with the term *mole* as applied to Avogadro's number of atoms or molecules, and with the *faraday*, 96,500 coulombs, which refers to the charge on $6.02 \times 10^{23}$ electrons. The term *einstein* refers to $6.02 \times 10^{23}$ photons. Finally, it might be emphasized that since the wave-number units ($cm^{-1}$) and frequency units ($sec^{-1}$) are directly proportional to all of the energy units, there is no reason why they cannot themselves be regarded as legitimate energy units. The wave number units, $\bar{\nu}$, in particular, are commonly used by spectroscopists as a measure of energy. It should be emphasized that when wave-number, frequency, or electron-volt units are used to express energies, these refer to the energies of individual particles, whether they be electrons, photons, or molecules.

Fundamental constants of interest here are summarized in Table 1 and energy interrelationships accurate to four significant figures are summarized in Table 2. Both tables are located at the end of this text. Although the use of Table 2 is straightforward, the student should gain some familiarity with the use and the magnitude of the different energy units which are characteristic of various molecular processes. Table 3, which is also located at the end of this text, lists atomic weights and isotope abundances of some of the more common elements.

## THE ELECTROMAGNETIC SPECTRUM

Many of the features of the electromagnetic spectrum, which will be of interest to us, are summarized in Fig. 1–4. Note that the energy increases from left to

| $\lambda$, Å | $10^8$ | $10^7$ | $10^6$ | $10^5$ | $10^4$ | $10^3$ | $10^2$ | 10 | 1 |
|---|---|---|---|---|---|---|---|---|---|
| $\bar{\nu}$, $cm^{-1}$ | 1 | 10 | $10^2$ | $10^3$ | $10^4$ | $10^5$ | $10^6$ | $10^7$ | $10^8$ |
| $\nu$, $sec^{-1}$ | $3\times10^{10}$ | | $3\times10^{12}$ | | $3\times10^{14}$ | | $3\times10^{16}$ | | $3\times10^{18}$ |
| $E$ erg/molecule | $2\times10^{-16}$ | | $2\times10^{-14}$ | | $2\times10^{-12}$ | | $2\times10^{-10}$ | | $2\times10^{-8}$ |
| kcal/mole | $2.86\times10^{-3}$ | | 0.286 | | 28.6 | | $2.86\times10^3$ | | $2.86\times10^5$ |
| electron volts | $1.24\times10^{-4}$ | | $1.24\times10^{-2}$ | | 1.24 | | $1.24\times10^2$ | | $1.24\times10^4$ |
| | Radio frequency | Micro-wave | | Infra-red | | Visible | Ultra-violet | | X-rays |
| Quantum effects: excitation of molecular... | | rotation | | vibration-rotation | | | electronic transition | | ionization |

**Fig. 1–4.** Summary of regions of the electromagnetic spectrum.

right. At the low energy end of the spectrum, in the radio frequency and microwave region, the result of direct absorption of this type of radiation by molecules leads to rotational excitation. In the infrared region, vibrational, accompanied by rotational, excitation occurs. In the visible and ultraviolet region, absorption of energy by molecules causes electronic transitions, in which valence electrons are promoted to higher energy orbitals, farther from the nucleus. This process is also accompanied by vibrational and rotational excitation. Finally, the x-rays cause ionization, that is, complete removal of an electron from the influence of the nucleus of the atom or nuclei of the molecule. If the x-ray has comparatively little energy, it removes a valence electron. High-energy x-rays can remove electrons from the lowest energy orbitals, next to the nuclei. All of these forms of excitation are conveniently regarded as quantum effects, in which an electromagnetic quantum is consumed which corresponds to the energy difference between the upper energy level $E_2$ and the lower energy level $E_1$ of the absorbing molecule. The molecule in turn is promoted from the lower to the upper level. Thus the absorption of energy results in an excitation process. Conversely, if a molecule is in an excited state, $E_2$, it may lose energy, emitted as $h\nu$, and drop to the lower energy state, $E_1$. Therefore, emission of radiation is the result of a de-excitation.

$$E_2 - E_1 = h\nu. \tag{1-6}$$

Equation (1–6) describes the energy relationship in the absorption or emission of a quantum of electromagnetic radiation; it applies equally well to rotational, vibrational, or electronic transitions in a molecule.

## EXPERIMENTAL TECHNIQUES

A typical spectrophotometer, that is, a device for recording a spectrum, consists of a spectral source, a dispersion medium, a detector, and an amplifier. The output of the amplifier may be fed to a meter or a recorder. If the detector and amplifier are replaced by a photographic plate, the instrument is called a spectrograph; whereas if they are replaced by the observer's eye, it is called a spectroscope. If one is interested in an emission spectrum, the spectral source should consist of some device which can excite the species of interest so that it will emit the desired spectrum. A discharge tube is commonly used as excitation source. The emitted light consists of lines of various wavelengths, the energies of which obey Eq. (1–6). To obtain an absorption spectrum, a source of continuous radiation, such as a tungsten filament lamp, is shone through a tube containing the sample of interest. Light of wavelengths that excite the sample to a higher energy state is absorbed and so does not reach the detector. Therefore, spectral lines also result from the absorption process and the energies of these lines also obey Eq. (1–6). The difference between the two types of spectra is comparable to that between negative and positive prints. The design of the components of a

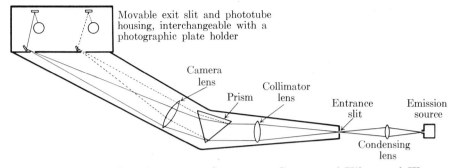

Movable exit slit and phototube housing, interchangeable with a photographic plate holder

Camera lens

Prism

Collimator lens

Entrance slit

Emission source

Condensing lens

**Fig. 1-5.** Diagram of a prism spectrophotometer. Courtesy of Hilger and Watts.

spectroscopic instrument are partially dependent upon the region of the spectrum in which one wishes to work. We shall start with a discussion of the region with which we are most familiar.

**The visible region.** The region to which the human eye is sensitive extends roughly from 4000 to 7000 Å, with the greatest sensitivity occurring in the yellow-green region, at about 5550 Å. A diagram of a typical prism spectrophotometer, designed for operation in this region, is shown in Fig. 1-5. Light from an emission source is focused by means of a condensing lens on the input slit of the spectrophotometer. Inside the spectrophotometer a collimator lens causes a parallel beam of radiation to shine upon the prism, where it is *refracted*; that is, it is broken into its component parts. Since the extent to which these components are separated is partly a function of the refractive

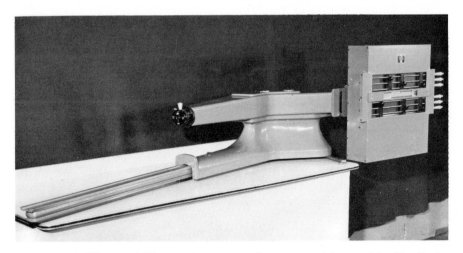

**Fig. 1-6.** A Hilger and Watts prism spectrophotometer with movable slit attachment. Courtesy of Hilger and Watts.

index of the prism material, glass with its higher refractive index is a better dispersion medium than quartz or fluorite. One wavelength of the disperse light, shown by the light solid lines in Fig. 1–5, is focused by a camera lens on the exit slit where it is reflected to a phototube. A shorter wavelength of light, shown by the dashed lines, is focused at a different point. For this particular instrument the spectrum is scanned by moving the exit slit and detector. A photograph of the spectrophotometer with optical bench and movable exit slit attachment is shown in Fig. 1–6. An alternative scanning design incorporates a fixed exit slit with a rotating prism. The spectro-photometer is readily converted to a spectrograph by replacing the slit and phototube detector device by a photographic plate in a suitable holder. An advantage of using photographic plates is that the spectrum can be amplified simply by lengthening the time of exposure; however, overexposure of the plates is a limiting factor.

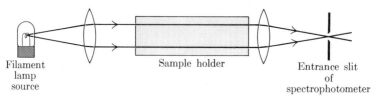

Filament
lamp
source
    Sample holder    Entrance slit
of
spectrophotometer

**Fig. 1–7.** Schematic representation of an apparatus designed to obtain an absorption spectrum.

For study of an absorption spectrum, the experimental arrangement shown in Fig. 1–5 is modified as shown in Fig. 1–7. A source of continuous radiation, usually a tungsten filament lamp, is converted into a parallel beam of radiation by a collimator lens. It shines through a sample tube containing the absorbing material, where specific wavelengths of light are absorbed. The light which is not absorbed is focused on the entrance slit of the spectro-photometer or spectrograph by a condensing lens in such a fashion that the collimator lens inside the spectrograph is filled with light.

It is convenient at this point to define a few terms which are used to describe the performance of spectroscopic apparatus. The *dispersion* of a spectrograph describes its ability to spread out light of different wavelengths. Consider light of two different wavelengths, differing by $\Delta\lambda$, emerging from a prism with an angle $\Delta\theta$ between them. The *angular dispersion* is defined as $\Delta\theta/\Delta\lambda$, or in the limit as $d\theta/d\lambda$. The *linear dispersion*, $\Delta x/\Delta\lambda$ or $dx/d\lambda$, measures the separation of light of different wavelengths on the focal plane and is related to the angular dispersion by

$$\frac{dx}{d\lambda} = l\frac{d\theta}{d\lambda},$$
(1–7)

where $l$ is the focal length of the instrument. Other factors being equal, the greater the dispersion of an instrument, the greater is its *resolving power*. The resolving power is the ratio of an observed wavelength to the smallest difference between two wavelengths which can be observed. In other words, if two spectral lines of average wavelength $\lambda$ just sufficiently separated by a wavelength difference $\Delta\lambda$ so that they can be distinguished, then $\lambda/\Delta\lambda$ expresses the resolving power of the instrument. The *actual resolving power* of an instrument is affected not only by the dispersion of the instrument, but by factors such as the input slit width, the accuracy of focusing, and the fineness of grain in a photographic plate. It is determined readily by experiment, and can vary from a few hundred to a million or more. The *theoretical resolving power* can be computed for any particular set of operating conditions and any particular design of instrument. For such computations we refer the reader to standard texts in experimental spectroscopy. The coincidence of actual and theoretical resolving powers reflects the excellence of design of an instrument and the skill of the experimentalist.

An alternative form of disperser can be used, namely, a diffraction grating, which as the name implies *diffracts* rather than refracts the incident radiation. There has been a revolution in the optics industry since the end of World War II, brought about by the perfection of the technique required to make replica gratings. Original gratings, usually of glass, must be machine-ruled with extreme precision and consequently are very expensive. However, many replica gratings, all of comparable quality to the original, can now be cast from one original grating. Many high-quality optical instruments are now being manufactured more cheaply with replica gratings than they could be made with prisms. Homemade spectroscopes, excellent for qualitative demonstrations, can be constructed for a few cents when plastic replica gratings are used.

For quantitative work, most diffraction grating spectrographs make use of a curved grating, which is silvered to act as a mirror. Many designs utilize the Rowland circle, named after the man at Johns Hopkins University who designed the first grating-ruling instrument, which was built in the latter part of the 19th century. The diameter of a Rowland circle is equal to the radius of curvature of the grating. With a slit source of radiation placed on one edge of the circle, all reflected images lie on other points of the circle. Figure 1–8 shows monochromatic radiation spreading in the distance from slit to grating, but being refocused at point $A$ on the circle. Light of slightly different wavelength is focused at a point adjacent to $A$. The ideal distance $d$ between rulings on a grating is given by

$$d = n\lambda/\sin\theta, \qquad (1\text{–}8)$$

where $\lambda$ is the average wavelength of the diffracted light, $\theta$ is the angle between the incident and departing rays, and $n$ is the *order* of the observed reflection. It has the same meaning as in the Bragg equation for x-rays. In principle,

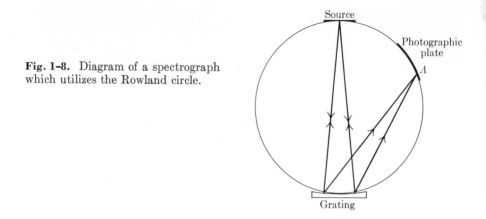

**Fig. 1–8.** Diagram of a spectrograph which utilizes the Rowland circle.

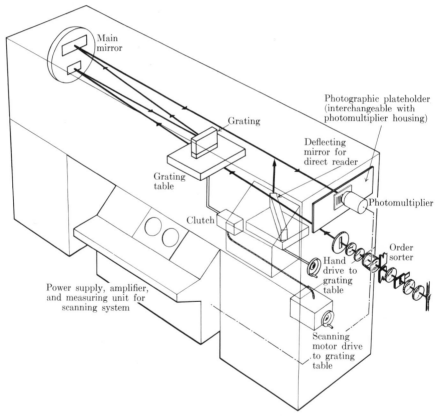

**Fig. 1–9.** Schematic diagram of an Ebert 3.4-meter grating spectrograph showing photographic, scanning and direct reading features. Courtesy of Hilger and Watts.

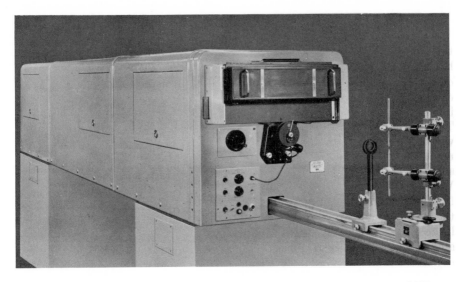

**Fig. 1-10.** An Ebert 3.4-meter grating spectrograph. Courtesy of Hilger and Watts.

for a fixed grating the slit and photographic plate can be placed at any position on the circumference of a Rowland circle. The diameter of the circle for a high resolution instrument may be 30 ft, so that there would be obvious space limitations if it were necessary to utilize the full circle. Modern spectrographs which incorporate curved gratings still utilize the principle of the Rowland circle, but they are usually of a much more compact design. For example, it may be possible to rotate both the grating and plate holder, and to move one along a track so that all positions on a Rowland circle can be obtained in a narrow space.

Another advantage of grating instruments is that spectra of higher order can be photographed readily. The interference patterns of the diffracted light are such that a line which appears at 2500 Å in first order ($n = 1$, Eq. 1-8) will appear at 5000 Å in second order ($n = 2$, Eq. 1-8). Thus the iron reference spectrum, which is not of much direct value for the red region of the spectrum, is commonly photographed in second order for this region. Higher-order spectra could also, of course, be troublesome. They can be eliminated by means of an order-sorter, such as a prism mirror or a series of filters, which allows only selected wavelengths to reach the grating. The angular dispersion of gratings is approximately linear in $\lambda$; that is, a grating has nearly the same dispersion over the entire spectral range, an important practical feature.

A drawing of an Ebert grating spectrograph, which utilizes a plane mirror grating, is shown in Fig. 1-9, and a photograph of the instrument is shown in Fig. 1-10.

If a spectrum is photographed, the next major problem is the determination of the wavelengths at which absorption occurs. A widely used instrument has a precise, printed wavelength scale which can be photographed directly on the plate. Another common procedure is to photograph a standard reference emission spectrum, such as from an iron hollow cathode tube or simple iron arc, directly under, or perhaps superimposed on, the spectrum of interest. The mechanics of obtaining the reference spectrum can be arranged in such a way that the optical system used to obtain the main spectrum of interest remains undisturbed. The positions of lines of both the main and reference spectra are then determined by use of some form of traveling microscope. Wavelengths of the spectrum of interest are then obtained by interpolation from lines of the reference spectrum. This can be a tedious procedure, since the distance on the photographic plate is usually not linear in either wavelength or energy units. In precise work, corrections for the refractive index of air, which is a function of wavelength, must be applied. All major spectroscopy laboratories have now automated the plate-reading procedure.

Two photographs of spectra obtained on instruments of widely different dispersion are shown in Fig. 1–11(a, b). Figure 1–11(a) is obtained on a prism instrument of low dispersion and low resolution. It can be seen from the printed wavelength scales that the linear dispersion of the prism instrument decreases with increasing wavelength. Individual emission lines are not

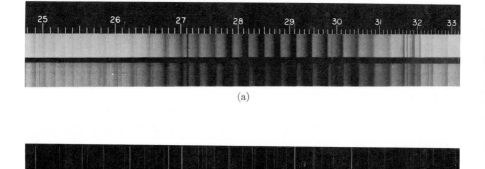

(a)

(b)

**Fig. 1-11.** (a) Two photographs of different exposure times obtained on a low resolution prism instrument of the absorption spectrum of $S_2$. Obtained by the flash photolysis of $H_2S_2$ using $CO_2$ as diluent. Black lines are absorption lines of atomic silicon obtained from the quartz windows. The printed scale is in hundreds of Angstrom units. Courtesy of R. Donovan, M. de Sorgo, O. P. Strausz and H. E. Gunning. (b) High-resolution photograph obtained on a 35-ft vacuum grating instrument in third order of one of the $\alpha$-bands of nitric oxide in emission. The spectrum was excited by a microwave discharge in air. Courtesy of A. E. Douglas.

resolved and partially overlap to form a series of bands.  In part (b) of the figure, each line of the spectrum is clearly resolved.

**The ultraviolet region.**  No modifications in principle are required to use spectrographs in the ultraviolet region, although we can no longer see any of the electromagnetic radiation.  In practice, certain instrumental components are no longer usable.  Glass rapidly becomes opaque in the ultraviolet region,

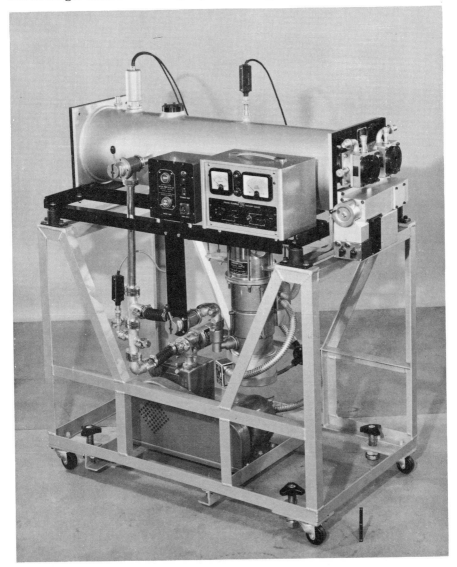

**Fig. 1–12.**  Photograph of a 1-meter normal incidence vacuum grating mono-chromator.  Courtesy of Hilger and Watts.

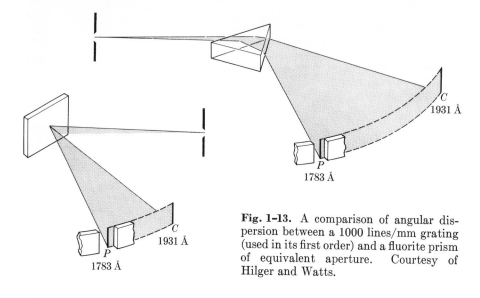

**Fig. 1–13.** A comparison of angular dispersion between a 1000 lines/mm grating (used in its first order) and a fluorite prism of equivalent aperture.    Courtesy of Hilger and Watts.

and so must be replaced by quartz optics.  Air itself becomes opaque at about 1800 Å, because of electronic transitions in oxygen.  These lead to atomic oxygen and hence ozone formation, the smell of which is readily detectable near a mercury arc lamp which has quartz windows.  Any high-energy, high-intensity u.v. source is capable of irreversibly denaturing protein, such as is present in the retina of the eye; so caution!  The practical result for spectroscopy of the opaqueness of air below 1800 Å is that the entire spectrograph must be contained in a chamber which can be evacuated (Fig. 1–12); hence the name *vacuum ultraviolet region*.  Tungsten lamps are inefficient sources of background continua in the u.v. region and are replaced by hydrogen lamps, or for higher energy sources, by xenon or helium lamps.  Prisms give much higher dispersion in the violet than in the red portion of the spectrum.  Therefore a fluorite prism might be used to advantage for work in the ultraviolet region (Fig. 1–13).  However, of the two instruments described in Fig. 1–13, the grating instrument would have much larger dispersion in the red region of the spectrum.  Furthermore, light cannot be transmitted by any known prism material below 1200 Å, so a reflection grating becomes a necessity.

**Photographic infrared.**  This region extends from about 8000 to 12,000 Å, and in both principle and practice it does not differ in any major fashion from the visible region.  A tungsten filament is an excellent source of continuous radiation.  The entire region, from x-rays to 12,000 Å, is referred to as the photographic region of the spectrum.  Different photographic emulsions are required for different regions of this spectrum, however.

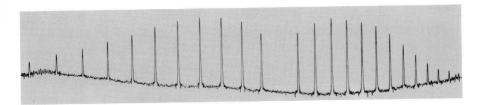

**Fig. 1-14.** High-resolution infrared absorption spectrum of the fundamental band of hydrogen bromide. The absorbance of infrared radiation as a function of the energy of radiation is shown. Courtesy of R. N. Swindlehurst.

**Infrared region.** Figure 1-1, which illustrated the experimental technique used to study blackbody radiation, is also a schematic representation of an infrared spectrometer, since a blackbody radiator is an excellent source of radiation in the infrared region. Silica glass transmits radiation greater than $2500 \text{ cm}^{-1}$ whereas rock salt, NaCl, is satisfactory for $\geq 600 \text{ cm}^{-1}$. For much lower-energy i.r. radiation, a reflection grating disperser must be used, since there is no known prism material which will transmit radiation in this region. Thermal detectors are used behind the exit slit. An example of an i.r. spectrum obtained on a recording spectrophotometer is shown in Fig. 1-14.

**The microwave region.** Different experimental techniques are required in this region, which bridges the gap between the i.r. and radio-frequency region. Antennas are used to transmit radiowaves, and can also be used in the microwave region. They are not satisfactory for spectral work, however. The source of microwave radiation is a klystron tube, which is under vacuum and in which standing waves are set up by electrons that oscillate in tune. These waves can be piped through a waveguide, also evacuated, in which the sample can be placed. A detector, such as a cat's whisker, connected to a crystal rectifier, signals the critical frequencies at which energy is absorbed by the sample. The klystron can be tuned, within limits, to give a range of frequencies, but to scan the entire microwave region, many different klystrons must be used.

We close our introduction with a brief discussion of some applications of spectroscopy.

**FLASH PHOTOLYSIS**

A secondary result of absorption of ultraviolet radiation is very often the rupture of chemical bonds, which can lead to formation of transient free radical species. In order to obtain the absorption electronic spectra of these very reactive molecules, a high concentration of them is required, which according to the mass action law means that their rate of disappearance is accelerated. The technique of flash photolysis, first used by Norrish and Porter, is designed for optimum efficiency in production and spectroscopic detection of free radicals. A bank of lamps capable of emitting ultraviolet light is placed around a quartz sample tube. Both lamps and sample tube are enclosed in a container which is made into an excellent reflector by a coating of magnesium oxide. The lamps are fired simultaneously from a bank of capacitors, which can store several hundred joules of energy. Steady nerves, or efficient earplugs, are prime requisites for this type of work. A second lamp, of lower energy, is triggered electronically in times of the order of microseconds or milliseconds after the original flash. The time interval between flashes can be adjusted so that the optimum concentration of transient species can be detected. The light from the second flash is reflected back and forth through the sample by mirrors to enhance its absorption before being focused on the slit of a spectrograph.

## MASERS AND LASERS

A practical application of spectroscopy of great current interest is in the field of masers and lasers. Pioneering work by Townes, Prokhorov, and Basov led to their award of the Nobel prize in physics for 1964. Maser is short for "microwave amplification by stimulated emission of radiation." For lasers, "microwave" is replaced by "light," which implies that they are of use in the visible region of the spectrum. The great advantage of these devices is that they can provide a parallel beam of *coherent* monochromatic radiation of much greater intensity than could be obtained previously. Only after the continuous radiation from a conventional source passes through a collimating lens, are the waves parallel and coherent. A further great loss in total intensity from a conventional light source occurs when a monochromator (e.g., prism and slit) is used to select light of a given frequency from a source of either continuous or discrete radiation. A laser circumvents these difficulties. The requisite for laser or maser action is a population "inversion," in which an excited state is populated more heavily than states of lower energy. We discuss one means whereby the necessary population inversion can be obtained. Figure 1–15 illustrates the energies of three electronic states, for example, of $Cr^{+++}$ ions in $Al_2O_3$, a ruby crystal. Atoms are excited from $E_1$ to $E_3$

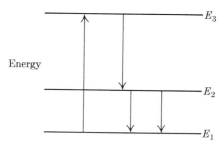

**Fig. 1-15.** Energy levels of $Cr^{+++}$, which can be used to obtain laser action.

by light of the appropriate frequency called the pumping frequency. Provided that the pumping action is great enough, a population inversion between levels of energy $E_2$ and $E_1$ is obtained despite naturally occurring transitions back to the ground state. An external signal of frequency $E_2 - E_1 = h\nu$ can trigger or stimulate a much stronger signal of the same frequency. The emission can be stored within the ruby by reflections, which set up standing waves of increasing amplitude. When these waves reach critical intensities, a precisely parallel beam of coherent, monochromatic radiation bursts through the end of the crystal. In some designs, mirrors outside the crystal are used to enhance the standing waves. Many different designs are now available, which use gases, liquids, or solids, from which one can obtain either continuous or pulsed radiation at a wide variety of wavelengths. These devices may well cause a revolution in the communications industry. (See Chapter 9 for discussion of spontaneous and stimulated emission.)

## STANDARDS OF LENGTH AND TIME

Because of the great precision possible in spectroscopic measurements, our standards of length and time have been redefined. In 1960, the 11th General Conference on Weights and Measures redefined the meter as 1,650,763.73 times the wavelength of the orange-red line of krypton-86 in vacuo. The old standard of length was a platinum-iridium bar. At the 12th General Conference in 1964, the second was redefined. It had previously been defined as a fraction of a mean solar year, that is, the average length of time it takes the earth to circle the sun. Since the absolute time in different years is not constant, this led to obvious difficulties in terms of practical precise measurements. The second is now defined in terms of the frequency of a transition in cesium-133, which is taken as 9,192,631,770 cycles/sec. Atomic clocks, based on the transition in atomic cesium, have been operated over a period of years with a precision of 1 part in 10 billion.

## PROBLEMS

1. Calculate the wavelength associated with:
   a) a 100-volt electron (ignore any possible relativistic effects);
   b) a one-ton automobile traveling at 60 mph.
2. Energy of quanta are given by $E = h\nu$. Why cannot this equation be applied to the results of the previous problem?
3. A photon is a particle with zero rest mass or capture mass. What is the effective mass of a photon in a monochromatic beam of 4000 Å wavelength?
4. The minimum energy required to dissociate one mole of $H_2$ into atoms is 103 kcal. Use values for the constants $h$, $c$, $N$, and $e$, and the mechanical equivalent of heat to express this energy in electron-volts, ergs/molecule, $cm^{-1}$, and $sec^{-1}$.

5. The rotational energy of a molecule of carbon monoxide, CO, is $1.91 \text{ cm}^{-1}$. Use the constants employed in the previous problem to express this in kcal/mole, electron volts, ergs/molecule, $\text{sec}^{-1}$, and megacycles/sec.

6. The ionization energy of nitrogen is 15.6 eV. Use the constants listed in Problem 4 to express this energy in kcal/mole, erg/molecule, $\text{cm}^{-1}$, and $\text{sec}^{-1}$.

7. Compute the optimum number of rulings per mm required for a grating where the mean angle between incident and reflected rays is 45°,

   a) for i.r. radiation of $1 \, \mu$;
   b) light of 6000 Å;
   c) u.v. radiation of 1000 Å.

## CHAPTER 2

# ROTATIONAL SPECTRA

Pure rotational spectra, that is, spectra which can be interpreted in terms of rotational energy levels only, are observed in the microwave or radio frequency region of the electromagnetic spectrum. Elaborate instrumentation is required for studies in these regions (Fig. 2–1), but the spectra obtained for heteronuclear diatomic molecules are simple to interpret. Unless a diatomic molecule is heteronuclear, that is, made of atoms of two different chemical elements, there is no polarity or dipole moment to the molecule. A rotating dipole generates an electric field which interacts with the electromagnetic radiation. Without a dipole moment, the molecule is virtually incapable of interacting with the microwave radiation.

The dumbbell model of the molecule, that is, consideration of the molecule as a rigid rotor, is entirely adequate for our purposes to explain the observed rotational spectrum. We shall start our discussions with the classical treatment of this model.

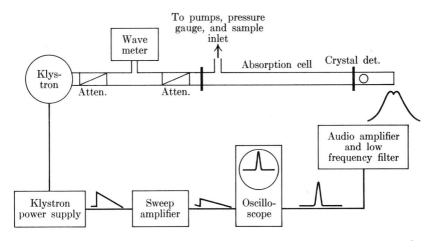

**Fig. 2–1.** Schematic representation of a microwave (video) spectrograph. From W. Gordy, W. V. Smith, and R. F. Trambarulo, "Microwave Spectroscopy," John Wiley and Sons (1953).

19

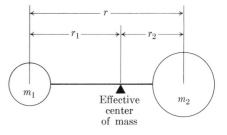

**Fig. 2–2.** Model of a rigid rotor, where $m_1$ and $m_2$ represent the masses of the two atoms. Since these are effectively the masses of the nuclei, the drawing is grossly out of scale.

## THE MOLECULE AS A RIGID ROTOR

Consider two atoms of masses $m_1$ and $m_2$ gm which are chemically bonded to form a diatomic molecule. Let the total distance between the centers of mass of the two atoms be $r$ cm, and let $r_1$ and $r_2$ be the distances of the atoms from the molecular center of gravity (Fig. 2–2). In general, the moment of inertia, $I$, of a system is given by

$$I = \sum_i m_i r_i^2, \tag{2–1}$$

and for our particular system

$$I = m_1 r_1^2 + m_2 r_2^2. \tag{2–2}$$

However, it is convenient to express $I$ in terms of $r$, rather than $r_1$ and $r_2$. This can be done by making use of a simple lever rule which says that for our system

$$m_1 r_1 = m_2 r_2;$$

$$\therefore r_1 = \frac{m_2}{m_1} r_2 = \frac{m_2}{m_1} (r - r_1), \tag{2–3}$$

which can be rearranged to give

$$r_1 = \frac{m_2}{m_1 + m_2} r. \tag{2–4}$$

Similarly,

$$r_2 = \frac{m_1}{m_1 + m_2} r. \tag{2–5}$$

Thus substitution of the results for $r_1$ and $r_2$, from Eq. (2–4) and (2–5), into Eq. (2–2) leads to

$$I = m_1 \left(\frac{m_2}{m_1 + m_2}\right)^2 r^2 + m_2 \left(\frac{m_1}{m_1 + m_2}\right)^2 r^2$$

$$= \frac{m_1 m_2}{m_1 + m_2} r^2$$

$$I = \mu r^2. \tag{2–6}$$

**Table 2-1**

ANALOGIES BETWEEN A LINEAR AND
ROTATIONAL SYSTEM

| Linear system | | Analog in a rotational system | |
|---|---|---|---|
| Mass | $m$ | Moment of inertia | $I = \mu r^2$ |
| Velocity | $v$ | Angular velocity (rad/sec) | $\omega$ |
| Momentum | $mv$ | Angular momentum | $M = I\omega$ |
| Kinetic energy $\frac{1}{2}mv^2$ | | Rotational kinetic energy $\frac{1}{2}I\omega^2$ | |

The term $m_1 m_2/(m_1 + m_2)$ is commonly called the reduced mass of the molecule, and given the symbol $\mu$. This terminology arises from the fact that our rotating two-particle system can now be treated by the same mathematics as that for a single particle of mass $m$ rotating about a fixed point. The only difference is that $m$ is replaced by $\mu$. The mathematics of a rotating system can be treated by methods completely analogous to those used for a linear system, as summarized in Table 2-1.

So far our treatment has involved classical or Newtonian mechanics. According to this treatment, all energies of rotation are possible. However, quantum mechanics tells us that only certain discrete rotational energy levels are possible. In other words, the rotational energies are quantized. The energies of these levels, in ergs, are given by

$$E = \frac{h^2 J(J+1)}{8\pi^2 \mu r^2} = \frac{h^2 J(J+1)}{8\pi^2 I}, \qquad (2\text{-}7)$$

$h$ is Planck's constant and $J$ is the rotational quantum number,* which is unitless and can have values

$$J = 0, 1, 2, 3, 4, \ldots \qquad (2\text{-}8)$$

According to classical theory,

$$E = \tfrac{1}{2}I\omega^2 = \frac{M^2}{2I}. \qquad (2\text{-}9)$$

Equations (2-7) and (2-9) can be combined to give

$$M = \frac{h}{2\pi}\sqrt{J(J+1)} \simeq \frac{h}{2\pi}J, \qquad (2\text{-}10)$$

* Equation (2-7) and the allowed values of $J$ are obtained by solving the Schrödinger wave equation for a rigid rotor. Standing waves which are functions of $J$ are associated with the rotating molecule. The wave equations, $\psi$, for rotation of a diatomic molecule are analogous to $\psi$ for $s$, $p$, $d$, $f$, $\ldots$ orbitals for electronic motion in atoms.

so that for any given value of $J$, the angular momentum $M$ can be calculated. The term $h/2\pi$ occurs so frequently in quantum theory that it is given the simpler symbol $\hbar$.

## OBSERVED ROTATIONAL SPECTRA

The experimentally observed spectrum in the very-low energy range of the electromagnetic spectrum consists of a series of absorption lines which are evenly spaced on an energy scale (Fig. 2–3). The fact that only certain discrete energies are absorbed by the molecule confirms the concept of quantization of energy. We shall now discuss a possible model for the rotational energy levels of the molecule which can account for the remarkably simple absorption spectrum. If the rotational levels allowed by quantum theory are given by

$$F(J),\ \text{cm}^{-1} = B_v J(J+1), \qquad (2\text{--}11)$$

then the energy levels shown in Table 2–2 and in Fig. 2–3 result. The term $B_v$ is a constant which must have units of cm$^{-1}$. Equation (2–7) can be converted to wave number units by dividing by $hc$:

$$E,\ \text{cm}^{-1} = \frac{hJ(J+1)}{8\pi^2 cI}. \qquad (2\text{--}12)$$

**Table 2–2**

ROTATIONAL ENERGY LEVELS GIVEN
BY $F(J) = B_v J(J+1)$

| $J$ | $F(\text{cm}^{-1})$ | First differences |
|:---:|:---:|:---:|
| 0 | 0 | |
| 1 | $2B_v$ | $2B_v$ |
| 2 | $6B_v$ | $4B_v$ |
| 3 | $12B_v$ | $6B_v$ |
| 4 | $20B_v$ | $8B_v$ |
| 5 | $30B_v$ | $10B_v$ |
| 6 | $42B_v$ | $12B_v$ |
| 7 | $56B_v$ | $14B_v$ |

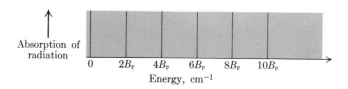

Absorption of radiation

0    $2B_v$    $4B_v$    $6B_v$    $8B_v$    $10B_v$

Energy, cm$^{-1}$

**Fig. 2–3.** Schematic representation of the pure rotational spectrum of a hetero-nuclear diatomic molecule.

It therefore follows, by comparison of Eq. (2–11) and (2–12) that

$$B_v = \frac{h}{8\pi^2 cI},$$ (2–13)

and therefore

$$I = \frac{h}{8\pi^2 cB_v}.$$ (2–14)

Now, if transitions are observed only between adjacent rotational energy levels, then only the transitions indicated by the vertical arrows shown in Fig. 2–4 can occur. The energies of these transitions correspond to the "first differences" shown in the third column of Table 2–2 and lead to the observed

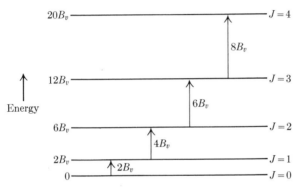

**Fig. 2–4.** Rotational energy levels for a diatomic molecule. Transitions caused by the absorption of radiation are indicated by vertical arrows.

absorption spectrum of Fig. 2–3. The restriction that $J$ can increase only by one unit for an absorption rotation spectrum does in fact apply, and is called a *selection rule*. It can be deduced from quantum mechanics but unfortunately cannot be demonstrated to apply experimentally from our simple results. (A perfectly random series of transitions would lead to the same spectral lines. However, the selection rule $\Delta J = \pm 1$ applies to vibration-rotation spectra, and is clearly shown in the observed spectra; see Fig. 3–4).

The constant $B_v$ is readily obtained from the observed spectrum, since the lines are evenly spaced at intervals of $2B_v$, and hence the moment of inertia of the molecule can be calculated. From this, the internuclear distance for a given molecule is easily obtained. The precision of the results in this region of the spectrum is fantastic. Values of $B_v$ to nine significant figures are readily obtained.* The present limitation in the determination of internuclear dis-

---

* For very precise work, a correction for centrifugal distortion of the molecule is required.

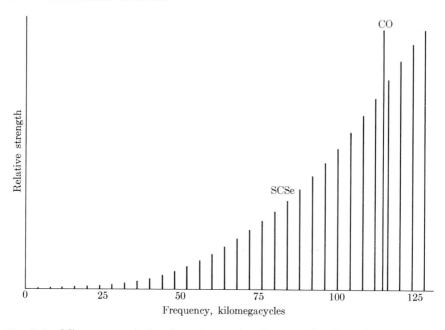

**Fig. 2–5.** Microwave rotational spectrum of a linear molecule with a relatively small (CO) and a relatively large (SCSe) moment of inertia. The second rotational line of CO (not shown) appears at 230 kilomegacycles. From W. Gordy, W. V. Smith and R. F. Trambarulo, "Microwave Spectroscopy," John Wiley and Sons (1953).

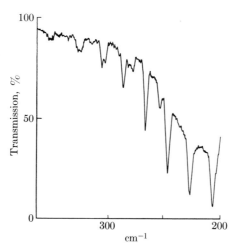

**Fig. 2–6.** Part of the pure-rotation infrared spectrum of HCl. Lines observed represent higher-$J$ rotational transitions which occur in the infrared region because of the small moment of inertia of the HCl molecule. From J. L. Hollenberg, *J. Chem. Ed.* **43,** 7 (1966), copyright by the *Journal of Chemical Education.*

tances is in the accuracy of Planck's constant. A representation of parts of two microwave spectra is shown in Fig. 2–5 and part of an actual pure rotational spectrum which just extends into the infrared region is represented in Fig. 2–6.

## PROBLEMS

1. What are the reduced masses for molecules of $Li_2$, $N_2$, AlH?

2. The spacing of a series of lines in the microwave spectrum of AlH is constant at 12.604 $cm^{-1}$. Calculate the moment of inertia, the internuclear distance of the AlH molecule. What is the energy of rotation when $J = 15$ in erg/molecule?

3. How many revolutions/sec does a $C^{12}O^{16}$ molecule make when $J = 1$, $J = 10$? $r = 1.128$ Å.

4. What is the rate of rotation of an AlH molecule in rad/sec, revolutions/sec, when $J = 15$? See Problem 2.

5. The $J = 1 \leftarrow 0$ transition of $HCl^{35}$ occurs at 6.264 × $10^5$ Mc/sec. Calculate the moment of inertia and internuclear separation of $HCl^{35}$.

6. The OH-radical has a moment of inertia of 1.480 × $10^{-40}$ g-cm$^2$.

   a) Calculate its internuclear distance. For $J = 5$, calculate
   b) its angular momentum;
   c) its angular velocity.
   d) Determine the energy absorbed in the $J = 6 \leftarrow J = 5$ transition in $cm^{-1}$ and erg/molecule.

7. Derive the expression for the moment of inertia of a classical rigid two-particle rotor.

8. The substitution of an isotopic atom has virtually no effect on internuclear distance.

   a) What is the significance of this in terms of the nature of the chemical bond?
   b) Calculate $B_v$ for $HCl^{37}$ from the data in Problem 5.

9. What is the change in $B_v$ when D, or $H^2$, is substituted for $H^1$ in the hydrogen molecule?

## CHAPTER 3

# VIBRATION-ROTATION SPECTRA

We shall now consider vibrational motion of the molecule. One might justifiably ask whether the rigid rotor model is adequate for the explanation of rotational spectra, when the molecule is known to vibrate. The answer is yes. As a first approximation the vibrational and rotational modes behave independently. For our purposes the only correction necessary to the results for rotational spectra is that the internuclear distance, $r$, is really a mean internuclear distance for the particular vibrational level in which the molecule is found. It might therefore be designated $r_v$, where $v$ stands for the vibrational quantum number, as it does in the constant $B_v$.

## THE MOLECULE AS A HARMONIC OSCILLATOR

The harmonic oscillator model of a diatomic molecule provides a satisfactory starting point for the discussion of vibrational motion. Again, we shall treat the model first from the classical standpoint. A harmonic oscillator is one which is acted upon by a force proportional to its displacement, $x$, from an equilibrium position. For a single particle which obeys simple harmonic motion, in other words, which obeys Hooke's law, we have

$$F \propto -x,$$

$$F = -kx = m\frac{d^2x}{dt^2} \tag{3-1}$$

$$\left( = -\frac{dV}{dx}, \quad \text{where } V \text{ is the potential energy} \right).$$

The proportionality constant $k$ has units of g/sec$^2$ or dynes/cm. Rearrangement of Eq. (3–1) leads to

$$\frac{d^2x}{dt^2} + \frac{k}{m}x = 0. \tag{3-2}$$

To solve this second-order differential equation, let $p = dx/dt$;

$$\therefore \frac{d^2x}{dt^2} = \frac{dp}{dt} = \frac{dp}{dx}\frac{dx}{dt} = p\frac{dp}{dx}; \tag{3-3}$$

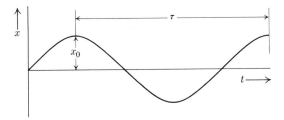

**Fig. 3–1.** The displacement, $x$, of a simple harmonic particle from its equilibrium position, as a function of time, $t$; $\tau$ is the time for one complete oscillation.

therefore

$$p \frac{dp}{dx} + \frac{k}{m} x = 0, \tag{3-4}$$

$$p\,dp = -\frac{k}{m} x\,dx,$$

$$p^2 = -\frac{k}{m} x^2 + C. \tag{3-5}$$

At the turning point, $p = dx/dt = 0$, and the position of maximum displacement can be designated $\pm x_0$. Therefore

$$C = \frac{k}{m} x_0^2; \tag{3-6}$$

$$\therefore \left(\frac{dx}{dt}\right)^2 = \frac{k}{m}(x_0^2 - x^2), \tag{3-7}$$

$$dx/dt = \sqrt{k/m}\,\sqrt{(x_0^2 - x^2)}, \tag{3-8}$$

$$\frac{dx}{\sqrt{x_0^2 - x^2}} = \sqrt{(k/m)}\,dt; \tag{3-9}$$

$$\therefore \arcsin(x/x_0) = \sqrt{(k/m)}\,t + C'. \tag{3-10}$$

Arbitrarily, when $t = 0$, $x = 0$; hence $C' = 0$. It follows that

$$\frac{x}{x_0} = \sin\sqrt{(k/m)}\,t, \tag{3-11}$$

$$x = x_0 \sin\sqrt{(k/m)}\,t; \tag{3-12}$$

$x_0$ is, in fact, the amplitude of the vibration (see Fig. 3–1).

When $t = \tau$, the molecule has completed one vibration. In other words, $\tau$ is the period of one vibration and corresponds to $2\pi$ rad. However, $\tau = 1/\nu$, where $\nu$ is the *frequency* of vibration in $\sec^{-1}$, that is, the number of vibrations/sec. Therefore, for one vibration $t = \tau$, and

$$x = x_0 \sin 2\pi. \tag{3-13}$$

Comparison of Eqs. (3–12) and (3–13) leads to

$$\sqrt{(k/m)}\,\tau = \sqrt{(k/m)}\,(1/\nu) = 2\pi,$$
$$\nu = (1/2\pi)\sqrt{(k/m)}\ \sec^{-1}. \tag{3–14}$$

An analogous treatment can be applied to a diatomic molecule. For one atom which is a distance $r$, other than its equilibrium distance, $r_e$, from its neighbor,

$$-k(r - r_e) = m_1 \frac{d^2 r_2}{dt^2}, \tag{3–15}$$

where $m_1$, $m_2$, $r_1$, and $r_2$ have the same significance as in Fig. 2–2. For the other atom,

$$-k(r - r_e) = m_2 \frac{d^2 r_2}{dt^2}. \tag{3–16}$$

But

$$r_1 = \frac{m_2}{m_1 + m_2}\,r \tag{2–4}$$

and

$$r_2 = \frac{m_1}{m_1 + m_2}\,r; \tag{2–5}$$

$$\therefore \frac{d^2 r_1}{dt^2} = \frac{m_2}{m_1 + m_2}\frac{d^2 r}{dt^2} \quad \text{and} \quad \frac{d^2 r_2}{dt^2} = \frac{m_1}{m_1 + m_2}\frac{d^2 r}{dt^2} \tag{3–17}$$

Thus both Eqs. (3–15) and (3–16) become

$$-k(r - r_e) = \frac{m_1 m_2}{m_1 + m_2}\frac{d^2 r}{dt^2}$$
$$= \mu \frac{d^2(r - r_e)}{dt^2} \quad \left(= -\frac{dV}{dr}\right). \tag{3–18}$$

The constant $r_e$ in the second derivative does not affect the equation, but is inserted for the sake of symmetry. Equation (3–18) for the diatomic molecule is completely analogous to Eq. (3–1) for the simple harmonic oscillator. It therefore follows that

$$\nu_{\text{vib}} = (1/2\pi)\sqrt{(k/\mu)}\ \sec^{-1} \tag{3–19}$$

is analogous to Eq. (3–14) for the simple harmonic oscillator. All of these expressions are for Newtonian motion. The classical potential energy of the diatomic harmonic oscillator is given by integration of Eq. (3–18):

$$V = \tfrac{1}{2}k(r - r_e)^2. \tag{3–20}$$

We must now consider the quantum restriction that only certain discrete amplitudes of vibration are allowed. According to quantum mechanics, for a molecule which executes harmonic motion,*

$$E, \text{ergs} = h\nu_{\text{vib}}(v + \tfrac{1}{2}). \qquad (3-$$

As we shall see in detail below, real molecules behave similarly to the pre ec-
tions of the harmonic model for small values of the vibrational quant
number, $v$. The approximation is given by

$$G(v), \text{cm}^{-1} = \omega_e(v + \tfrac{1}{2}). \qquad (3-$$

The notation, $G(v)$, shows that the vibrational energy is a function of $v$, wh
can have the values

$$v = 0, 1, 2, \ldots \qquad (3-$$

From Eqs. (3–21) and (3–22), with proper regard for units, it follows that

$$\omega_e = \nu_{\text{vib}}/c. \qquad (3-2$$

## OBSERVED VIBRATION-ROTATION SPECTRA

Again our discussion is limited to heteronuclear diatomic molecules, sin
infrared vibration-rotation spectra are observed only if the diatomic molecu
has a dipole moment. Here it is more convenient to discuss the energy leve
involved first and the form of the observed spectra later.

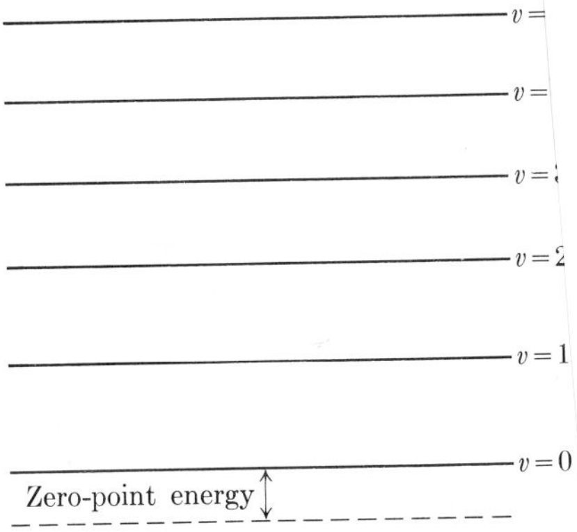

**Fig. 3-2.** Vibrational energy levels for a diatomic molecule. Contraction in the spacing is somewhat exaggerated.

Equation (3–22) predicts that, for $v = 0$, the molecule still has vibrational
energy. This is the so-called zero-point energy of the molecule, the meaning
of which will become more clear in our discussion of potential energy functions
(see Chapters 4 and 5). The equation also predicts that the vibrational energy
levels are evenly spaced. As a first approximation this is true, but in fact the
spacings decrease somewhat as $v$ increases (see Fig. 3–2). An equation which

---

* Equations (3–21) and (3–23) are obtained by solving the Schrödinger equation
for a harmonic oscillator.

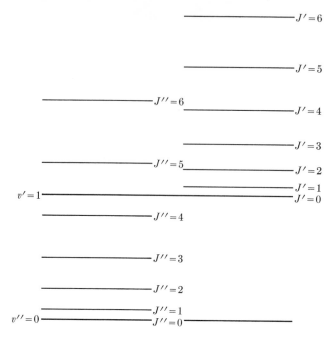

**Fig. 3-3.** Rotational levels associated with two vibrational levels of a diatomic molecule. Lower-state levels are indicated by double primes and upper-state levels by single primes.

accounts satisfactorily for the observed contraction of energy levels is

$$G(v) = \omega_e(v + \tfrac{1}{2}) - \omega_e x_e(v + \tfrac{1}{2})^2, \tag{3-25}$$

where $\omega_e x_e$ is a constant in wave number units and where $\omega_e \gg \omega_e x_e$. Thus the second term in the equation, since it involves a small constant and a $(v + \tfrac{1}{2})$-squared term, only becomes appreciable for higher values of $v$. We have seen that $\omega_e$ is a constant for harmonic motion, and it is correct to regard $\omega_e x_e$ as an anharmonic term; that is, a term which corrects for the observed deviations from harmonic motion.* Now for every vibrational level, there are associated rotational levels (see Fig. 3-3). The total vibration-rotation energy of a molecule with a given $v$ and $J$ can be obtained simply by adding the vibrational and rotational energy. Therefore, from Eqs. (2-11) and (3-25),

$$F(J) + G(v) = B_v J(J + 1) + \omega_e(v + \tfrac{1}{2}) - \omega_e x_e(v + \tfrac{1}{2})^2. \tag{3-26}$$

---

* Anharmonicity of vibration might be understood in terms of mutual repulsion of the two nuclei, which becomes the dominant term for small internuclear distances. Thus for vibrations of large amplitude, the internuclear axis can be extended more readily than it can be compressed, and Hooke's law is no longer obeyed.

The factor $B_v$ is a constant for a given vibrational level only, and it decreases slightly with increasing $v$. Thus, if we obtained a vibration-rotation spectrum for molecules where the transitions involve the levels at which $v = 0$ and $v = 1$, we should be able to deduce both $B_0$ and $B_1$ from the observed spectrum. It should be noted that at equilibrium at room temperature most molecules, except very heavy ones, predominantly have $v = 0$.

The small change in $B_v$ as a function of $v$ is a reflection of the slight interdependence of vibrational and rotational energies. The change in $B_v$ is a correction for the assumption that vibrational and rotational energies are additive.

For a vibration-rotation spectrum, transitions are observed from rotational levels of one vibrational state to rotational levels of another vibrational state. We shall concern ourselves with absorption spectra only, where the transition is to higher-energy states. (In principle there is nothing different in the treatment of emission spectra.) The *selection rule* governing the transitions is $\Delta J = \pm 1$.* For example, a molecule with $v = 0$, $J = 3$ can be promoted to the level with $v = 1$, $J = 2$ or the level with $v = 1$, $J = 4$. The operation of the selection rule is clearly shown in Fig. 3-4. The lower level involved in an observed transition is designated with a double prime, and the upper level with a single prime. The lines of the spectrum in which $\Delta J = J' - J'' = -1$ are designated the *P*-branch and those in which $\Delta J = J' - J'' = +1$ are called the *R*-branch. All the lines of both branches form a *vibration-rotation band*. By convention, all the lines which make up the band are designated in terms of the branch to which they belong and the *lower*-state rotational quantum number. Thus the spectral line which corresponds to the transition from the energy level with $v = 0$, $J'' = 3$ to the level with $v = 1$, $J' = 2$ is the $P(3)$ line; the line corresponding to the transition from the level with $J'' = 1$ to the level with $J' = 2$ is the $R(1)$ line.

The form of an infrared spectrum is shown schematically in the lower part of Fig. 3-4, and reproductions of high resolution spectra are shown in Figs. 1-14 and 3-5.† As the infrared energy is increased, there is a slight contraction in the spacing of the spectral lines. As a first approximation, this contraction may be ignored, which as we shall see, is equivalent to the assumption that $B'_v = B''_v$. Furthermore, there is a gap in the observed band, which is commonly called the null gap or zero line. This missing line would

---

* From Eq. (2-10) it can be seen that angular momentum is quantized approximately in units of $h/2\pi$. If photons have $\pm 1$ unit of angular momentum, then the selection rule $\Delta J = \pm 1$ follows from the law of conservation of momentum.

† We plot absorbance in the positive $y$-direction vs. wave number in the positive $x$-direction, since the energies of absorbed light waves describe the absorption spectra in direct and fundamental terms. There is a convention in which transmittance is plotted in the positive $y$-direction vs. wavelength in the positive $x$-direction or vs. the wave number in the *negative* $x$-direction (eg., Fig. 2-6). Figures 1-14 and 3-5 can be converted to the latter convention by rotation of the spectra through 180°.

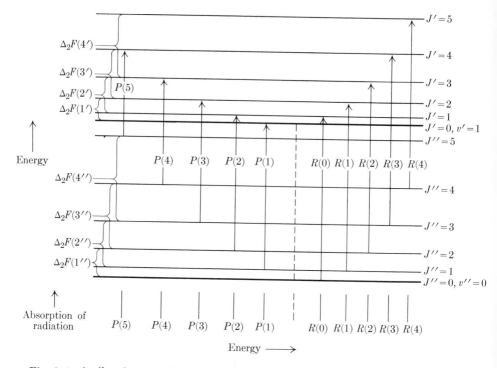

**Fig. 3–4.** A vibration-rotation energy-level diagram, showing some of the observed transitions. The form of the observed spectrum is indicated at the bottom of the figure. The contraction of spacings of spectral lines is greatly exaggerated, whereas the spacing between $v = 1$ and $v = 0$ is often greater.

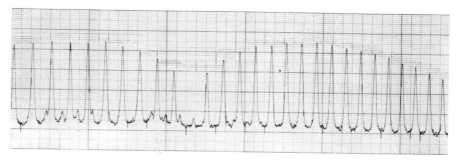

**Fig. 3–5.** High-resolution spectrum of the fundamental band of CO, showing absorbance vs. energy. Note the null gap and the contraction of the spacing between lines with increasing energy. Courtesy of R. N. Swindlehurst.

correspond to the $(J' = 0) \leftarrow (J'' = 0)$ transition if it could occur; i.e., if it did not violate the selection rule $\Delta J = \pm 1$. By convention, the upper state of an observed transition is designated first, so that an arrow pointing to the left indicates an absorption spectrum, and an arrow to the right, an emission spectrum.

## SIMPLIFIED VIBRATION-ROTATION BAND

We assume that $B'_v = B''_v$ and therefore we shall simply use the symbol $B$. Both upper- and lower-state rotational levels are given by $F(J) = BJ(J + 1)$. However, for the $P$- and $R$-branches, $J' \neq J''$ and therefore we must distinguish between upper- and lower-state rotational quantum numbers. A common pitfall for students first exposed to spectroscopy is to confuse energy levels with *transitions between* energy levels. It is the latter which is directly observed by experiment. If we avoid this pitfall, all that follows should be straightforward.

In general, the upper-state energy levels, in $cm^{-1}$, are given by

$$T' = F(J') + G(v')$$
$$= BJ'(J' + 1) + G(v'), \qquad (3\text{--}27)$$

and the lower-state levels by

$$T'' = F(J'') + G(v'')$$
$$= BJ''(J'' + 1) + G(v''). \qquad (3\text{--}28)$$

Since $J'$ and $J''$ have specific relationships for the $P$- and $R$-branches, equations for these branches are greatly simplified if they are expressed in terms of the lower-state $J$-values only.

For the $P$-branch, $J' - J'' = -1$. Therefore $J' = J'' - 1$. The upper-state equation thereby becomes

$$T'(P) = BJ''(J'' - 1) + G(v'). \qquad (3\text{--}29)$$

Subtraction of Eq. (3–28) from Eq. (3–29) leads to the following equation for the energy of the $P$-branch lines:

$$P(J'') = T' - T'' = -2BJ'' + \bar{\nu}_{00}, \qquad J'' = 1, 2, 3, \ldots, \qquad (3\text{--}30)$$

where the term $\bar{\nu}_{00} = G(v') - G(v'')$ corresponds to the zero line.

Similarly, for the $R$-branch, $J' - J'' = +1$. Therefore $J' = J'' + 1$, and the equation for upper-state energy levels becomes

$$T'(R) = B(J'' + 1)(J'' + 2) + G(v'). \qquad (3\text{--}31)$$

Subtraction of the lower-state energy equation (3–28) from Eq. (3–31) leads to

$$R(J'') = T' - T'' = 2BJ'' + 2B + \bar{\nu}_{00}, \qquad J'' = 0, 1, 2, \ldots \qquad (3\text{--}32)$$

Since energy differences corresponding to $P$- and $R$-branch lines are always expressed in terms of the lower-state value of $J$, we shall henceforth drop the double-prime notation for $P(J)$ and $R(J)$.

Equations (3–30) and (3–32) predict a vibration-rotation band which consists of equispaced lines, the energy difference between which, if the hypothetical null gap line is assumed to exist, is always $2B$. Our simplified model therefore leads to a picture of a vibration-rotation band which is remarkably similar to that for a pure rotation spectrum. The chief differences are the missing line in the sequence and the appearance of the vibration-rotation band in a higher-energy region of the electromagnetic spectrum.

Let us examine the significance of the null gap, $\bar{\nu}_{00}$, more closely. We see from the equations for both the $P$- and $R$-branches that the energy in wave number units of $\bar{\nu}_{00}$ is given by

$$\bar{\nu}_{00} = G(v') - G(v'')$$
$$= \omega_e(v' + \tfrac{1}{2}) - \omega_e x_e(v' + \tfrac{1}{2})^2 - \omega_e(v'' + \tfrac{1}{2}) + \omega_e x_e(v'' + \tfrac{1}{2})^2. \quad (3\text{–}33)$$

This, in fact, is the energy difference between *rotationless* upper and lower states, where $J'' = J' = 0$, or in other words, the energy spacing between pure vibrational levels. For the band corresponding to the $(v' = 1) \leftarrow (v'' = 0)$ transition, called the *fundamental band*,

$$\bar{\nu}_{00} = \tfrac{3}{2}\omega_e - \tfrac{9}{4}\omega_e x_e - \tfrac{1}{2}\omega_e + \tfrac{1}{4}\omega_e x_e$$
$$= \omega_e - 2\omega_e x_e \quad (3\text{–}34)$$
$$\simeq \omega_e.$$

If the transition $(v' = 2) \leftarrow (v' = 0)$, called the *first overtone*, is also observed, then both $\omega_e$ and $\omega_e x_e$ can be determined accurately from Eq. (3–33).

We are now in a position to give a quantitative treatment of observed vibration-rotation bands, which is also applicable to electronic band spectra.

### EXACT TREATMENT OF A VIBRATION-ROTATION BAND

Since for a vibration-rotation band, $B'_v < B''_v$, this inequality must be taken into account for an exact treatment. The general equations for energies of upper and lower states now become (cf. Eqs. 3–27 and 3–28)

$$T' = B'_v J'(J' + 1) + G(v'), \quad (3\text{–}35)$$
$$T'' = B''_v J''(J'' + 1) + G(v''). \quad (3\text{–}36)$$

Again, for the particular case of the $P$-branch, $J' = J'' - 1$, so that from Eq. (3–35)

$$T'(P) = B'_v J''(J'' - 1) + G(v'). \quad (3\text{–}37)$$

Subtraction of Eq. (3–36) from Eq. (3–37) and collection of terms in the same

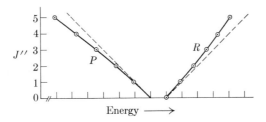

**Fig. 3-6.** Plot of $J''$ vs. energy for $P$- and $R$-branches for a few values of $J''$. The dashed straight lines represent the corresponding plot if $B'_v = B''_v$.

power of $J''$ gives the energies of the $P$-branch lines:

$$P(J) = (B'_v - B''_v)J''^2 - (B'_v + B''_v)J'' + \bar{\nu}_{00}, \qquad J'' = 1, 2, 3, \ldots \quad (3\text{-}38)$$

A similar treatment for the $R$-branch gives

$$T'(R) = B'_v(J'' + 1)(J'' + 2) + G(v'), \qquad\qquad\qquad\qquad (3\text{-}39)$$
$$R(J) = (B'_v - B''_v)J''^2 + (3B'_v - B''_v)J'' + 2B'_v + \bar{\nu}_{00},$$
$$J'' = 0, 1, 2, \ldots \quad (3\text{-}40)$$

in analogy with Eqs. (3-31) and (3-32).

These exact equations for both branches are, in fact, equations for parabolas. We know that the $P$- and $R$-branches must be interrelated, since they have common upper and lower states. We shall now show that they can be fitted to the same parabolic equation. The operation, illustrated in Figs. 3-6 and 3-7, consists of (a) taking the mirror image of the $P$-branch, which is performed by making the substitution $m = -J''$; and (b) shifting the $R$-branch one unit upward, performed by the substitution $m - 1 = J''$.

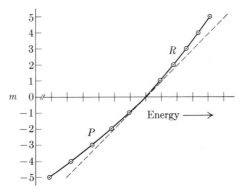

**Fig. 3-7.** A parabolic plot composed of the first few lines of the $P$- and $R$-branches. Energy $= (B'_v - B''_v)\ m^2 + (B'_v + B''_v)\ m + \bar{\nu}_{00};\ m = -J''$ for the $P$-branch; and $m = J'' + 1$ for the $R$-branch. If $B'_v = B''_v$, the dashed straight line would result. The curvature is considerably exaggerated for an i.r. band.

These substitutions convert Eqs. (3–38) and (3–40), respectively, into

$$P(m) = (B_v' - B_v'')m^2 + (B_v' + B_v'')m + \bar{\nu}_{00}, \qquad (3\text{–}41)$$

$$R(m) = (B_v' - B_v'')(m - 1)^2 + (3B_v' - B_v'')(m - 1) + 2B_v' + \bar{\nu}_{00}. \qquad (3\text{–}42)$$

Simplification of the above $R$-branch equation reduces it to the identical form of the $P$-branch equation (3–41). A plot of the common equation (3–41) is shown in Fig. 3–7. The energy of the null gap is given by the point corresponding to $m = 0$. Equation (3–41) can be rewritten in the form

$$\text{Energy (cm}^{-1}) = am^2 + bm + c, \qquad (3\text{–}43)$$

where

$$a = (B_v'' - B_v'),$$
$$b = B_v'' + B_v',$$
$$c = \text{null gap.}$$

The constant $a$ is small and negative. Therefore the curvature of the parabola is slight. However, if the plot is shown for large enough values of $m$, the vertex of the parabola eventually must occur in the $R$-branch. Moreover, if the constant $a$ is larger, then the curvature to the parabola is much more marked, and the vertex becomes readily apparent. The latter is commonly the case for electronic band spectra, which will be discussed in detail in Chapter 4.

## INFRARED BAND ANALYSIS

The assignment of the correct rotational quantum numbers to a vibration-rotation band is an easy task, since the null gap is readily observed. However, the calculation of precise $B_v'$ and $B_v''$ values from the observed contracted band is not quite so obvious. For convenience, we recall here that the energy of both branches is given by

$$\text{Energy, } T = (B_v' - B_v'')m^2 + (B_v'' + B_v')m + \nu_{00}, \qquad (3\text{–}41)$$

$$T = am^2 + bm + c, \qquad (3\text{–}43)$$

where $m = \cdots, -3, -2, -1, 0, 1, 2, 3, \ldots$; the negative values of $m$ correspond to $P$-branch lines, and the positive values, to $R$-branch lines. Consider the values of $T$ shown in Table 3–1 and the first and second differences for lines of both the $P$- and $R$-branches. From these differences, one can in principle obtain the constants $a$ and $b$, and hence $B_v'$ and $B_v''$. In practice, this procedure is not very precise; a linear graphical method, or the comparable algebraic procedure, is more precise in all cases, and these latter methods also are better for making arithmetic mistakes apparent. The standard procedure which has been developed to obtain the rotational constants of both upper and lower states is that of finding *combination differences*, which are given the symbol $\Delta_2 F(J)$, (delta two $F$ of $J$). From a study of Fig. 3–4, we

**Table 3-1**

FIRST AND SECOND ENERGY DIFFERENCES FOR THE LINES
OF A BAND SPECTRUM (EITHER VIBRATION-ROTATION OR
ELECTRONIC)

| $m$ | $T$ | First difference | Second difference |
|----|-----|------------------|-------------------|
| $-5$ | $25a - 5b + c$ | | |
| | | $9a - b$ | |
| $-4$ | $16a - 4b + c$ | | $2a$ |
| | | $7a - b$ | |
| $-3$ | $9a - 3b + c$ | | $2a$ |
| | | $5a - b$ | |
| $-2$ | $4a - 2b + c$ | | $2a$ |
| | | $3a - b$ | |
| $-1$ | $a - b + c$ | | $2a$ |
| | | $a - b$ | |
| $0$ | $c$ | | $2a$ |
| | | $-a - b$ | |
| $+1$ | $a + b + c$ | | $2a$ |
| | | $-3a - b$ | |
| $+2$ | $4a + 2b + c$ | | $2a$ |
| | | $-5a - b$ | |
| $+3$ | $9a + 3b + c$ | | $2a$ |
| | | $-7a - b$ | |
| $+4$ | $16a + 4b + c$ | | $2a$ |
| | | $-9a - b$ | |
| $+5$ | $25a + 5b + c$ | | $2a$ |
| | | $-11a - b$ | |
| $+6$ | $36a + 6b + c$ | | |

see that for nearly every line in the $P$-branch, $P(J + 1)$, there is a corresponding line in the $R$-branch, $R(J - 1)$, with a common upper-state level. Subtraction of the energy difference corresponding to the $P(J + 1)$ line from that of the $R(J - 1)$ line gives the energy difference, $\Delta_2 F(J'')$, between the $(J + 1)$ and $(J - 1)$ levels of the lower state.*

$$R(J - 1) = B'_v J'(J' + 1) - B''_v J''(J'' - 1) + \bar{\nu}_{00}, \qquad (3\text{-}44)$$

$$P(J + 1) = B'_v J'(J' + 1) - B''_v(J'' + 1)(J'' + 2) + \bar{\nu}_{00}, \qquad (3\text{-}45)$$

$$\Delta_2 F(J'') = 4B''_v(J'' + \tfrac{1}{2}). \qquad (3\text{-}46)$$

Therefore, a plot of $\Delta_2 F(J'')$ vs. $J''$ has a slope of $4B''_v$. By rearrangement of Eq. (3-46), we obtain

$$4B''_v = \frac{\Delta_2 F(J'')}{(J'' + \tfrac{1}{2})}, \qquad (3\text{-}47)$$

from which the method of numerical computation of $B''_v$ from all $\Delta_2 F(J'')$ values is apparent. Similarly, the $R(J)$ and $P(J)$ lines have common lower states, so that combination differences of these lines, $\Delta_2 F(J')$, eliminate the

---

* We use the notation $\Delta_2 F(J'')$, rather than the conventional $\Delta_2 F''(J)$, to emphasize that $J''$ has the same meaning on both sides of Eq. (3-46). Similarly, $J'$ has the same meaning on both sides of Eq. (3-50). The value of $J$ in any equation for $\Delta_2 F(J)$ is most simply regarded as $J$ of the midlevel of the three rotational levels involved in the combination difference. Thus $\Delta_2 F(5'')$ is the energy difference between the sixth and fourth rotational levels associated with the lower vibrational state. Similarly, $\Delta_2 F(2')$ is the energy difference between the third and first rotational levels of the upper vibrational state.

lower-state energies and enable one to determine $B'_v$:

$$R(J) = B'_v(J' + 1)(J' + 2) - B''_v J''(J'' + 1) + \bar{\nu}_{00}, \qquad (3\text{-}48)$$

$$P(J) = B_v J'(J' - 1) - B''_v J''(J'' + 1) + \bar{\nu}_{00}, \qquad (3\text{-}49)$$

$$\Delta_2 F(J') = 4B'_v(J' + \tfrac{1}{2}), \qquad (3\text{-}50)$$

$$4B'_v = \frac{\Delta_2 F(J')}{(J' + \tfrac{1}{2})} . \qquad (3\text{-}51)$$

## SUMMARY OF BAND ANALYSIS

We have seen how the fundamental rotational constant, $B_v$, for both upper and lower vibrational states, can be obtained from a vibration-rotation band observed under high resolution. We have also seen how the vibrational constant, $\omega_e$, can be approximately determined from a $1 \leftarrow 0$ vibrational transition (the fundamental band). If both the fundamental and first overtone (the latter is the $2 \leftarrow 0$ transition) are observed under high resolution, then $\omega_e$ and $\omega_e x_e$ can be determined precisely.

So far we have considered gas phase spectroscopy, where, under high resolution, transitions between individual rotational levels can be observed. The same is true if the absorbing molecule is dissolved in a completely inert solvent. More commonly however, only the absorption bands can be seen in solution and not the individual lines of the band. In such cases, a lower-resolution instrument may be preferable, since it makes possible the "scanning" of larger regions of the infrared spectrum.

For polyatomic molecules, bending or "wagging" vibrational modes are possible in addition to the "stretching" modes, which we have discussed in some detail. Different chemical groups, such as

have characteristic absorption energies for their fundamental vibrational modes, which to a considerable extent are independent of chemical environment; and these energies can be used for identification purposes. It has been said that a good infrared spectrum, which can be obtained in less than an hour, is often the equivalent of one month's conventional laboratory work to an organic chemist. Studies of changes in absorption intensities and spectral shifts when one changes from inert to polar solvents are providing fundamental information about solute-solvent interactions and hydrogen bonding.

## PROBLEMS

1. The simple harmonic force constant for a molecule is virtually independent of any factor other than electrostatic interactions. One of the fundamental vibrational modes of $H_2O$ occurs at $3652\ \mathrm{cm}^{-1}$. Predict the frequency of the corresponding mode in $D_2O$ and in $H_2O^{18}$.

2. The simple harmonic force constant for $DCl^{35}$ is $4.903 \times 10^5$ dynes/cm. Calculate $\omega_e$ in $cm^{-1}$. How many vibrations/sec does DCl make? Is this dependent on $v$, assuming that the harmonic approximation is valid?

3. The values of $\omega_e$ in $cm^{-1}$ are 4395, 3817, and 3118, respectively, for the molecules $H_2$, HD, and $D_2$. Calculate the approximate zero-point energies for each of these molecules in kcal/mole. The values of $\omega_e x_e$ in $cm^{-1}$ are 118, 95, and 64, respectively, for the same molecules. Calculate the exact zero-point energies in kcal/mole. Would one observe an infrared spectrum for any of these molecules? Why?

4. The mean of the internuclear distances for $HCl^{35}$ in the $v = 0$ and $v = 1$ levels is 1.293 Å. Calculate the difference in $cm^{-1}$ between the $R(0)$ and $P(1)$ lines of the fundamental band for $HCl^{35}$.

5. The fundamental band for CO is centered at 2143.3 $cm^{-1}$, and the first overtone, at 4259.7 $cm^{-1}$. Calculate $\omega_e$, $\omega_e x_e$, the simple harmonic force constant, and the number of vibrations per sec.

6. The fundamental band for $DCl^{35}$ is centered at 2011.00 $cm^{-1}$. Assume that the internuclear distance is constant at 1.288 Å, and calculate the wave number of the first two lines of each of the $P$- and $R$-branches of $DCl^{35}$.

7. If the mean internuclear distance of $HCl^{35}$ were constant, the following data would describe some of the lines of the $(v = 1) \leftarrow (v = 0)$ (fundamental) band. Assign the proper labels to all of the lines, and calculate $B$ and $r$. Calculate $\omega_e$, assuming that the molecule is a harmonic oscillator, and hence obtain a value for the harmonic force constant in dynes/cm.

| $cm^{-1}$ |
| --- |
| 2906.3 |
| 2927.5 |
| 2948.7 |
| 2969.9 |
| 3012.2 |
| 3033.4 |
| 3054.6 |
| 3075.8 |

8. Repeat Problem 7 on the following data for the fundamental band of $C^{12}O^{16}$.

| $cm^{-1}$ |
| --- |
| 2154.77 |
| 2158.63 |
| 2162.49 |
| 2166.35 |
| 2174.07 |
| 2177.93 |
| 2181.79 |
| 2185.65 |

9. Given that $\omega_e$ and $r_e$ are 1580 cm$^{-1}$ and 1.207 Å for $O^{16}O^{16}$, calculate the maximum displacement $(r - r_e)$ in Å as a percentage of $r_e$, when $v = 0$, $v = 15$. Assume that the molecule is a harmonic oscillator.

10. Repeat problem 9 for $H_2$, given that $\omega_e = 4395$ cm$^{-1}$ and $r_e = 0.742$ Å.

11. The following precise data applies to the fundamental band of HBr. Note that the isotope effect for $Br^{79}$ compared to $Br^{81}$ is too small to affect the observed results. Using combination differences, analyze the data to obtain $B_1$, $B_0$ and the null gap. Report the values of $\Delta_2F(8')$ and $\Delta_2F(3'')$.

| Wave numbers in vacuo | |
| --- | --- |
| 2371.71 | 2575.52 |
| 92.50 | 91.33 |
| 2412.83 | 2606.70 |
| 32.72 | 21.61 |
| 52.15 | 36.07 |
| 71.13 | 50.08 |
| 89.66 | 63.63 |
| 2507.73 | 76.74 |
| 25.36 | 89.39 |
| 42.53 | 2701.59 |

# ELECTRONIC SPECTRA

In this chapter we shall be concerned with electronic potential-energy wells, the interrelationship between electronic and vibrational motion, and the spectra observed when transitions occur between different electronic states of diatomic molecules.

### ATOM COMBINATIONS; POTENTIAL-ENERGY WELLS

Let us consider two atoms, each of which has a single unpaired electron in its orbital of lowest allowed energy. At infinite distance from each other, these atoms possess considerable potential energy, namely, the potential energy of chemical bond formation. As the atoms approach each other, the attractions of each nucleus for the electron of the other atom begin to become important and the potential energy approaches a minimum.* At the minimum, a compromise exists between repulsive and attractive forces of electrons and nuclei. Considerable overlap of atomic orbitals exists. At smaller internuclear distances, repulsive forces become predominant and the potential-energy curve rises steeply (see Fig. 4–1). The depth of the potential-energy minimum (Fig. 4–1) below the asymptote represents the strength of the chemical bond, or as it is more precisely called, the bond-dissociation energy, $D_e$. This is the energy required to separate two atoms from their equilibrium internuclear distance, $r_e$, to infinite distance from each other.

When the two atoms approach each other, they of course possess some kinetic energy. Since the total energy of the system must at all times be constant, any increase in potential energy must result in a decrease in kinetic energy, and conversely. Thus the kinetic energy is at a maximum when the potential energy is at a minimum, which occurs at the equilibrium internuclear distance, $r_e$. Therefore the two approaching atoms have ample energy to approach even more closely and to climb the left-hand side of the potential-energy well. The atoms will climb until all of the energy of the system is

---

* Particles at infinite distance have zero potential energy in mechanics problems. The standard chemists' and spectroscopists' procedure of assigning arbitrarily zero potential energy to the molecule at its equilibrium internuclear distance is followed here.

41

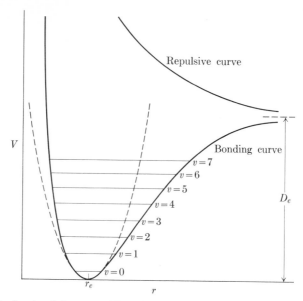

**Fig. 4–1.** Plot of potential energy, $V$, vs. internuclear distance, $r$, for a light, singly bonded diatomic molecule. The upper curve is the repulsive curve and the lower one, the bonding curve. The dashed parabola is the curve for a harmonic oscillator. The spacing of the first few vibrational levels is shown. This spacing is considerably closer for a heavy molecule.

converted into potential energy, i.e., to a height above the asymptote exactly equal to their kinetic energy at infinite separation. They then reverse their path.* Thus the two atoms have in fact existed as a molecule for exactly one vibration, and they then have flown apart. As we can calculate from Eq. (3–19), the period of one vibration is of the order of $10^{-13}$ sec. However, in any real system, many more species than two atoms are present, and if during the $10^{-13}$-sec interval, a collision with a third body occurs, some energy can be removed from the two atoms, they then become trapped in the potential-energy well, albeit still with nearly enough energy to escape from the well. Further collisions remove more energy, however, and eventually a molecule with a small amount of vibrational energy results. For atoms, the third body may be the wall of the containing vessel, a molecule, or even another atom. For the combination of two free radicals to form a polyatomic molecule another important possibility exists, and this is the flow of energy from the newly formed bond into other "internal degrees of freedom," that is, other vibrational modes within the same molecule. This alternative method of trapping molecules within stable potential-energy wells is of importance

---

* In other words, they run uphill until they are out of gas, and then coast back down and out of the well.

for methyl radical combinations to form ethane, so that they do not always require a third body in order to form stable ethane molecules. Thus the rate of combination of polyatomic free radicals is much greater than the rate of combination of atoms.

The above discussion for approaching atoms is applicable to the case where the electron spins are opposite, so that the two electrons can form a stable chemical bond by occupying the same molecular orbital. In this case electrostatic attractive forces are dominant. However, if the electrons of the approaching atoms have parallel spins, the electrostatic repulsions are dominant and the electrons do not share a single molecular orbital. The atoms then approach along the upper potential-energy curve, which has no minimum (see Fig. 4-1), until all of their kinetic energy of translation has been converted to potential energy, whereupon the reverse process occurs. As will be discussed in later chapters, the molecular electronic wave functions have entirely different forms for the different electron spin states.

## RELATION BETWEEN ELECTRONIC AND VIBRATIONAL ENERGY

The shape of the potential-energy well can, in principle, be calculated using the Schrödinger equation of wave mechanics. Terms are required which express the magnitude of the repulsive and attractive potential energies of all electrons and nuclei for one another. The Born-Oppenheimer approximation simplifies the calculation, since it states that the internuclear distance need not be treated as a variable. This approximation states that the electrons move so fast relative to the nuclei, that the electron cloud adjusts instantly to any change in internuclear distance. For any given internuclear distance, $(r - r_e)$, a unique solution can be found to the electronic Schrödinger equation, and by repeating the problem for sufficient values of $(r - r_e)$, the shape of the well is obtained. In practice, a precise calculation is extremely tedious, even for the hydrogen molecule. Such a wave-mechanical calculation will not be of further concern to us here. Two important conclusions we wish to draw from the above discussion are: First, by means of the Born-Oppenheimer approximation, it is possible to separate electronic and vibrational motions of the molecule. The latter, by definition, are concerned with changes in $(r - r_e)$. Second, the *potential* energy of vibration is electronic in nature. Vibrational energy levels, given by Eq. (3–25), are shown in Fig. 4–1. These energy levels represent total energy of vibration, both kinetic and potential, corresponding to each particular value of the vibrational quantum number, $v$. The points of intersection of these levels with the potential-energy well represent classically the turning points in the vibrations of molecules, and hence the points at which kinetic energy of vibration is zero. Therefore at these turning points, the magnitudes of potential energy of vibration and electronic potential energy are identical, *when both are measured from the bottom of the potential-energy well.*

In Chapter 3, we saw that if a diatomic molecule obeys Hooke's law, then the restoring force, $F$, is given by

$$-F = \frac{dV}{dr} \tag{3-1}$$

$$= k(r - r_e), \tag{3-18}$$

and the potential energy, $V$, is given by

$$V = \tfrac{1}{2}k(r - r_e)^2. \tag{3-20}$$

From the above discussion we see that the magnitude of the restoring force constant, $k$, is determined *solely* by electronic interactions.

Equation (3-20) for $V$ is that of a parabola, shown as a dashed line in Fig. 4-1. It can be seen that it provides a good approximation to the correct potential-energy well for small values of $(r - r_e)$, but the error becomes increasingly large for larger displacements. The fact remains that the correct restoring force constant, although not harmonic in nature, is caused solely by electronic effects. It follows that the shape of potential-energy wells for molecular isotopes, such as $H_2$ and $D_2$, are identical, although the spacing of vibrational levels shows a mass effect (see the section on vibrational isotope effect in this chapter). The form of the observed potential energy, $V$, can be expressed quite precisely and most simply in terms of the Morse function,

$$V = D_e(1 - e^{-\beta(r-r_e)})^2, \tag{4-1}$$

where $V$ is the potential energy and $D_e$, the bond-dissociation energy. In the exponential term, $(r - r_e)$ in cm is the displacement from the equilibrium internuclear distance; $\beta$ is obtained by substituting Eq. (4-1) into the vibrational Schrödinger equation, and is given by

$$\beta = 1.2177 \times 10^{-7} \omega_e \sqrt{\mu/D_e}. \tag{4-2}$$

Both $\omega_e$, the harmonic vibrational constant, and $D_e$ are expressed in wave number units, $cm^{-1}$, and the reduced mass, $\mu$, is expressed in atomic mass units, for example, exactly 6 for $C^{12}C^{12}$.

## POTENTIAL-ENERGY WELLS INVOLVING ELECTRONIC EXCITATION

Let us now consider the case where a molecule is formed by two combining atoms, one of which is electronically excited; that is, it has a valence electron promoted into an orbital farther from the nucleus. The excited atom possesses considerably more potential energy than a ground-state atom, and this must be accounted for in a potential energy vs. internuclear distance diagram. The asymptote of the resultant Morse curve will be higher than that for two electronic ground-state atoms by the energy of electronic excitation of the one atom, $A_{\text{exc}}$ (Fig. 4–2). The bond-dissociation energy and equilibrium inter-nuclear distance will also be different for the molecule formed by the com-bination of one excited and one ground-state atom. In short, a different molecule results from two combining atoms when one of the atoms is elec-tronically excited. The resultant electronically excited molecule has, to be sure, the same molecular weight and the same number of electrons as the ground-state molecule, but because it has a different distribution of its electron cloud, all properties associated with its chemical bond are different. The excited molecule's electronic energy is designated by $T_e$, the difference between the minimum in its potential-energy well and that of the electronic ground state (Fig. 4–2). In general, a new potential-energy curve results from every combination of atoms in different electronic states.

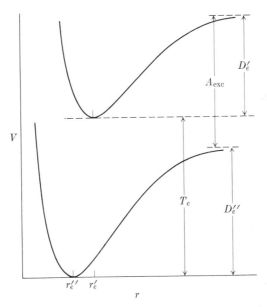

**Fig. 4–2.** Potential-energy wells for a ground-state molecule and an electronically excited molecule.

So far, we have considered only the formation of an electronically excited molecule by the combination of two atoms, one of which at least has been electronically excited by some means, perhaps by the absorption of a light quantum of precisely the right energy, $h\nu$. There is no reason, other than *selection rules*, why light of appropriate wavelength cannot cause direct excitation of a ground electronic-state molecule to an excited electronic state. For purposes of this discussion we shall assume that the electronic transition is *allowed* and we shall postpone until later a discussion of the selection rules.

## ELECTRONIC TRANSITIONS

Let us consider a molecule in its electronic ground state, with $v = 0$. The molecule possesses a total vibrational energy of approximately $\omega_e$ wave number units. When it reaches either turning point in its oscillation, its kinetic energy is zero and the total vibrational energy is in the form of potential energy. However, the *total* vibrational energy as a function of internuclear distance is constant and is represented by the horizontal line labeled $v = 0$ in Fig. 4–1. We must consider the total vibrational energy of the electronic ground state when we discuss the events that occur upon absorption of a light quantum which is of appropriate frequency to cause an electronic transition.

What then are the specific details of an allowed electronic transition? First of all, at room temperature nearly all molecules have $v = 0$, so that jumps to an excited electronic state occur from points near the bottom of the electronic ground-state potential-energy well. Second, since harmonic oscillators spend most of their time near their turning points, jumps can be regarded on a simple probability basis as occurring from points *on* the ground-state potential-energy curve.* Third, momentum must be conserved, and therefore jumps occur to turning points on the upper curve; that is, the atoms in the molecule have zero-displacement velocity and hence zero momentum both before and after the electronic transition. Finally, the time required to excite one electron is negligibly small compared to the period of one vibration (the latter is $\simeq 10^{-13}$ sec!). This means that jumps occur vertically on a $V$ vs. $r$ diagram, such as in Fig. 4–3, since $r$ does not change detectably during the time of transition. The latter restriction is known as the *Franck-Condon principle*. The end result of the excitation process depends partly on $r_e''$ and $r_e'$, the equilibrium internuclear distances of the ground and excited states. When $r_e'' \simeq r_e'$ (Fig. 4–3a), the molecule is excited to low-lying vibrational levels of the excited state, where the net result may simply be a return to the ground state with emission of the absorbed light; or, if intervening electronic states exist, transitions to these states may occur with emission of light of lower energy (longer wavelength). Alternatively, the excited molecules, if they have sufficiently long lifetimes, may upon collision transfer all or part of their energy to the collision partner by a radiationless

---

* Quantum theory differs from the above classical considerations. For the case where $v'' = 0$, quantum theory predicts that jumps are most likely to occur from the midpoint of the oscillation. Quantum theory also explains why the zero-point energy is finite. If it were zero, then both the position and momentum of the nuclei would be sharply defined, which is a violation of the Heisenberg uncertainty principle. Since the maximum displacement is smallest for $v'' = 0$, the difference between the two theories is not drastic. Observed spectra can be described adequately by assuming that all transitions occur from turning points on one potential-energy curve to turning points on another.

transition. Similar results are observed if $r''_e > r'_e$, except that higher vibrational levels of the excited state are populated upon absorption.

On the other hand, if $r''_e < r'_e$, then transitions to the excited state occur to portions of the left-hand side of the upper-state potential-energy well, some of which are above the asymptote (Fig. 4–3b). Therefore for these cases, neglecting third-body effects, the molecule dissociates in the time of a half-vibration.

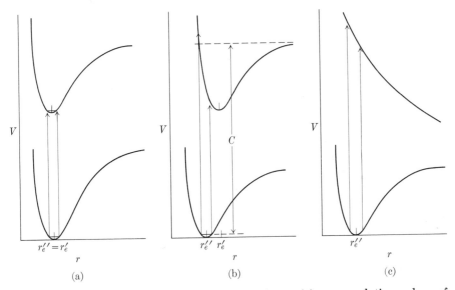

**Fig. 4–3.** Plots showing dependence of observed transitions on relative values of equilibrium internuclear distances for upper and lower electronic states. (a) A discrete spectrum results. (b) Transitions involving more energy than $C$ result in dissociation, and a continuous spectrum is observed. Transitions with less energy than $C$ result in a discrete spectrum. (c) A continuum is observed for all transitions to a repulsive potential-energy curve.

There are important differences in the observed absorption spectrum depending upon whether the absorption process does or does not provide enough energy for dissociation of the electronically excited molecule to occur. If not enough energy is supplied for dissociation of the electronically excited state, then transitions are occurring from discrete rotational and vibrational levels associated with the ground electronic state to discrete rotational and vibrational levels of the excited state. The result is a discrete spectrum, which consists of a series of bands. The same rotational selection rule we discussed earlier often applies, namely $\Delta J = \pm 1$, although there are no restrictions on $\Delta v$ other than those imposed by the Franck-Condon principle. It is important to note that for the discrete spectrum, even though much more energy is absorbed than that of the dissociation energy of the ground electronic-state molecule, no dissociation of the molecule occurs.

If the absorption process does lead to dissociation of the *excited* electronic state, then the endpoint of the transition corresponds to points on the left-hand side of the upper-state potential-energy curve that are above the asymptote. We discussed earlier how two combining atoms also arrive at the same points, namely, by momentarily transforming all of their kinetic energy of translation into potential energy of vibration. Since a continuous distribution of kinetic energy occurs, then all possible positions on the potential energy curve above the asymptote are attainable.* Similarly, by absorption of light by ground-state molecules, a continuum of positions above the asymptote of the upper-state potential-energy curve is attainable. In other words, if the absorption process results in sufficient energy to dissociate the electronically excited molecule, it involves transitions to a continuum of energy levels. Therefore light is absorbed of all wavelengths corresponding to amounts of energy larger than the critical amount required for dissociation of the electronically excited state, as contrasted to the discrete or selective absorption of radiation for the nondissociative process. Therefore the onset of the continuum in an absorption spectrum can be used to calculate the bond-dissociation energy, $D'_e$, of the excited electronic state, provided that $T_e$, the energy difference between the potential energy minima of the two electronic states, is known. Similarly, the onset of a continuum in an emission spectrum can be used to obtain the bond-dissociation energy of the lower electronic state, provided that sufficient other information is available.

For all transitions which occur *to* a potential energy curve which has no minimum, called a *repulsive* curve, only a continuous spectrum will be observed, and molecular dissociation into atoms will occur. This is true for both an absorption process (Fig. 4–3c) or for an emission process. Naturally, if a spectrum has no discrete portion, then no information about bond dissociation energies can be obtained.

## ELECTRONIC-BAND SPECTRA; ROTATIONAL ANALYSIS

We shall for now restrict our discussion to electronic bands which consist only of $P$- and $R$-branches. Since electronic excitation is involved, the energy differences between upper and lower states is much greater than for a vibration-rotation band, the electronic spectrum commonly being observed in the visible or ultraviolet region of the spectrum. Since the total energy can be separated into its components, we can write for the energy of the upper

---

* Quantum calculations show that "particle-in-the-box" kinetic energy levels for atoms are so closely spaced for a reasonably sized container that they are virtually continuous.

(electronically excited) state*

$$T' = T_{rot} + T_{vib} + T_{elect}, \tag{4-3}$$

$$T' = B'_v J'(J' + 1) + \omega'_e(v' + \tfrac{1}{2}) - \omega_e x'_e(v' + \tfrac{1}{2})^2 + T_{elect}, \tag{4-4}$$

where $T_{elect}$ is the energy required to promote a valence electron from its ground-state molecular orbital to its higher-energy molecular orbital, as measured from minima of potential-energy wells. For the lower electronic state, both the rotational and vibrational constants are different:

$$T'' = B''_v J''(J'' + 1) + \omega''_e(v'' + \tfrac{1}{2}) - \omega_e x''_e(v'' + \tfrac{1}{2})^2. \tag{4-5}$$

There is no electronic term for the lower state if it is the ground electronic state of the molecule. For the rotational analysis of a band, however, we may rewrite Eqs. (4-4) and (4-5) as

$$T' = B'_v J'(J' + 1) + c', \tag{4-6}$$

$$T'' = B''_v J''(J'' + 1) + c''. \tag{4-7}$$

Appropriate conversion of Eq. (4-6) for the particular cases of $P$- and $R$-branches and subtraction of Eq. (4-7) is analogous to the treatment of a vibration-rotation band. Thus the form of an electronic band is identical to that of a vibration-rotation band. Only the last term, $c'$, of the upper-state equation has different meaning. Similarly, the conversion from $J$ to $m$ in the equations for $P$- and $R$-branches is identical for electronic and vibration-rotation bands, resulting in the general equation

$$T = T' - T'' = am^2 + bm + c, \tag{3-43}$$

where $a = (B'_v - B''_v)$, $b = (B''_v + B'_v)$, $c = \bar{\nu}_{00}$. Positive values of $m$ correspond to the $R$-branch, and negative values to the $P$-branch. We saw in Table 3–1 that by taking first and second differences on the values of $T$, it was possible in principle to obtain the constants $a$ and $b$, but in practice the analysis was made more precise by determining the combination differences, $\Delta_2 F(J)$. There was no problem in the correct assignment to spectral lines in a vibration-rotation band where the location of the null gap is obvious. The precise analysis of an electronic band can be performed by determining combination differences, once the lines are identified, but the correct labeling of spectral lines is a more difficult problem. The reason is that the difference between $B'_v$ and $B''_v$ is nearly always much greater for an electronic band than a vibration-rotation band, and commonly $B'_v$ is appreciably less than $B''_v$. This means that $r'_v$ is appreciably greater than $r''_v$. The constant $a$ of the para-

---

* The wave equation corresponding to Eq. (4–3) is $\psi_{tot} = \psi_{rot}\psi_{vib}\psi_{elect}$, which states that the total wave equation can be factored into its component parts.

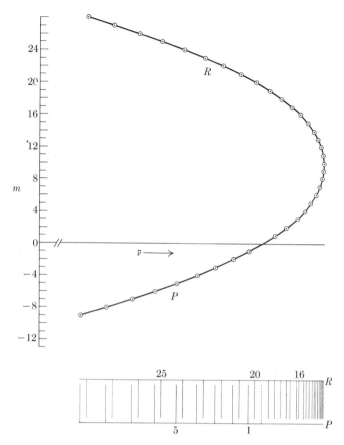

**Fig. 4-4.** Fortrat parabola for an electronic band. The corresponding spectrum shown below is obtained by extrapolating the observed points on the parabola onto the energy axis. For simplicity, $R$-branch lines are shown above, $P$-branch lines below, in the spectrum.

bolic equation (3–43) is now much greater, so that a plot of $m$ vs. energy gives a much more sharply curved parabola in which the vertex is readily apparent. Such a plot is shown in Fig. 4–4; it is called a Fortrat parabola. The observed spectrum is obtained by extrapolating all the points on the parabola onto the energy ($\bar{\nu}$) axis. Now the $P$- and $R$-branches overlap. The striking spectral feature is no longer the null gap, which may not be apparent at all, but rather the band head. However, the null gap must be located before the correct assignments can be made to the observed lines. We shall proceed to this problem shortly, but a few other features of an electronic band merit description. Actual electronic spectra with $P$- and $R$-branches are shown in Fig. 4–5. Since the vertex or head of the parabola occurs in the $R$-branch, the latter is sometimes called the head branch. Conversely, the $P$-branch is also

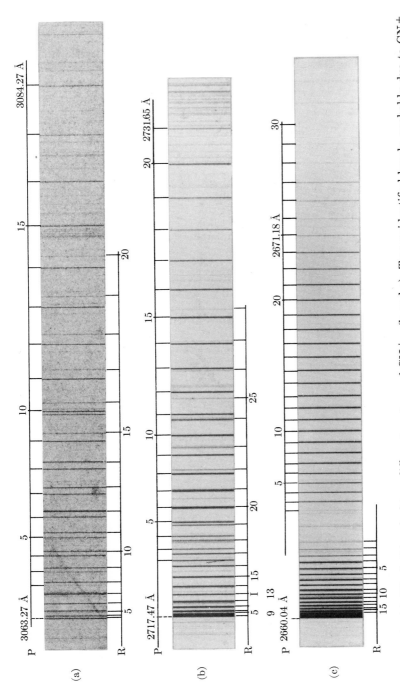

**Fig. 4-5.** (a) The 1–0 band of two different systems of CN$^+$. (b and c) Two unidentified bands, probably due to CN$^+$. These emission spectra were excited by passing an electric discharge through a tube of helium containing traces of (CN)$_2$. They were photographed on a 21-foot grating spectrograph having a linear dispersion in the first order of 2.5 Å/mm. From A. E. Douglas and P. M. Routly, *Astrophys. J.* **119**, 303 (1954).

called the tail branch. A common description of this type of band is the phrase "degraded to the red," which means that as one moves from the head to the tail of the band, one is moving away from the violet end of the spectrum *toward the red part* of the spectrum. In principle there is no reason why $B_v'$ should not be considerably larger than $B_v''$ for electronic spectra, and in practice this is sometimes observed. This results in the constant $a$ of Eq. (3–43) being large and positive. The resulting Fortrat parabola is "degraded to the violet" and the band head is contained in the $P$-branch (reverse the parabola in Fig. 4–4 so that the vertex is closer to the ordinate than the tail of the parabola, and locate the vertex below the energy axis). No fundamental principle is changed for analysis of such bands.

The fact that one can, in principle, obtain the constants $a$ and $b$ by taking first and second differences does suggest how the analysis of an electronic band can be performed where the correct assignment of $J''$ or $m$ values is not readily apparent. If one takes an enlarged photograph of an electronic band, and uses a pair of calipers, it becomes an easy matter to separate lines of the two branches. Usually there is a region in the tail of the band where a few spectral lines appear to belong to one branch, that is, they appear to contract a consistent amount as one moves toward the band head. If this is so, the screw on the calipers must be tightened a constant amount as one moves them from one adjacent pair of lines to the pair next closest to the head which has a line in common with the previous pair. By means of the constant contraction of the calipers (constant second difference), one can usually follow the lines of one branch into the band head, and then by constant expansion of the calipers, continue on the lines back out to the tail again. The missing line, corresponding to the null gap, is usually then readily apparent. Once it is located, the correct assignment of all spectral lines is then straightforward, and the determination of the combination differences, and hence $B_v'$ and $B_v'$, is no more difficult than for a vibration-rotation band.

### ELECTRONIC BAND SPECTRA; VIBRATIONAL ANALYSIS

From the rotational analysis of electronic bands, band-origin differences, $\bar{\nu}_{00}$, are obtained, that is, energy differences between pairs of vibrational levels belonging to different electronic states, which do not involve any rotational energy. From band-origin data, $\bar{\nu}_{00}$, one can obtain the vibrational constants, $\omega_e$ and $\omega_e x_e$, which, it should be emphasized, are different for different electronic states. The energy of the vibrational levels associated with an excited electronic state, referred to the minimum in the ground-state potential-energy curve, are given by

$$G(v') = T_e + \omega_e'(v' + \tfrac{1}{2}) - \omega_e x_e'(v' + \tfrac{1}{2})^2, \qquad (4\text{–}8)$$

where $T_e$ is the difference in energy between the minima in the two potential-energy curves (Fig. 4–2). The energy of the vibrational levels of the electronic ground state are given by

$$G(v'') = \omega_e''(v'' + \tfrac{1}{2}) - \omega_e x_e''(v'' + \tfrac{1}{2})^2. \qquad (4\text{-}9)$$

Therefore the energy differences are given by

$$\bar{\nu}_{00} = T_e + \omega_e'(v' + \tfrac{1}{2}) - \omega_e x_e'(v' + \tfrac{1}{2})^2 - \omega_e''(v'' + \tfrac{1}{2}) + \omega_e x_e''(v'' + \tfrac{1}{2})^2.$$
$$(4\text{-}10)$$

For an absorption spectrum, the lower-state vibrational quantum number is usually equal to zero. The transitions from $v'' = 0$ to various $v'$ levels thus constitute a progression of bands denoted as the $v'' = 0$ progression. The energies required to observe the first five members of this progression, tabulated in Table 4–1, are obtained simply by substituting $v'' = 0$ and $v' = 0, 1, 2, 3, \ldots$ into Eq. (4–9). From Table 4–2 it can be seen that $\omega_e x_e'$ is equal to one-half of the second differences between adjacent bands. Once $\omega_e x_e'$ is known, then $\omega_e'$ is readily obtained from the first differences.

Because absorption spectra frequently involve only the $v'' = 0$ level, they often yield more information about the excited electronic state than the ground electronic state. Conversely, one might expect emission spectra to

Table 4–1

ENERGIES OF BAND ORIGINS FOR A $v'' = 0$ PROGRESSION

| Transition $v' \leftarrow v''$ | Energy required to observe transition | First difference | Second difference |
|---|---|---|---|
| $0 \leftarrow 0$ | $T_e + \tfrac{1}{2}\omega_e' - \tfrac{1}{4}\omega_e x_e' - \tfrac{1}{2}\omega_e'' + \tfrac{1}{4}\omega_e x_e''$ | $\omega_e' - 2\omega_e x_e'$ | |
| $1 \leftarrow 0$ | $T_e + \tfrac{3}{2}\omega_e' - \tfrac{9}{4}\omega_e x_e' - \tfrac{1}{2}\omega_e'' + \tfrac{1}{4}\omega_e x_e''$ | $\omega_e' - 4\omega_e x_e'$ | $2\omega_e x_e'$ |
| $2 \leftarrow 0$ | $T_e + \tfrac{5}{2}\omega_e' - \tfrac{25}{4}\omega_e x_e' - \tfrac{1}{2}\omega_e'' + \tfrac{1}{4}\omega_e x_e''$ | $\omega_e' - 6\omega_e x_e'$ | $2\omega_e x_e'$ |
| $3 \leftarrow 0$ | $T_e + \tfrac{7}{2}\omega_e' - \tfrac{49}{4}\omega_e x_e' - \tfrac{1}{2}\omega_e'' + \tfrac{1}{4}\omega_e x_e''$ | $\omega_e' - 8\omega_e x_e'$ | $2\omega_e x_e'$ |
| $4 \leftarrow 0$ | $T_e + \tfrac{9}{2}\omega_e' - \tfrac{81}{4}\omega_e x_e' - \tfrac{1}{2}\omega_e'' + \tfrac{1}{4}\omega_e x_e''$ | | |

Table 4–2

ELECTRONIC BAND-ORIGIN DATA (cm$^{-1}$) FROM AN EMISSION SPECTRUM

| $v'$ \ $v''$ | 0 | 1 | 2 | 3 | 4 |
|---|---|---|---|---|---|
| 0 | 29,647.5 | 28,167.5 | 26,707.5 | 25,267.5 | |
| 1 | 30,407.5 | 28,927.5 | 27,467.5 | 26,027.5 | 24,607.5 |
| 2 | 31,127.5 | 29,647.5 | 28,187.5 | 26,747.5 | 25,327.5 |
| 3 | 31,807.5 | 30,327.5 | 28,867.5 | 27,427.5 | 26,007.5 |
| 4 | 32,447.5 | 30,967.5 | 29,507.5 | | |
| 5 | | 31,567.5 | 30,107.5 | 28,667.5 | |
| 6 | | | 30,667.5 | 29,227.5 | 27,807.5 |
| 7 | | | | 29,747.5 | 28,327.5 |

yield more information about the lower electronic state. However, emission spectra commonly arise from a wide population distribution of excited electronic state vibrational levels, so that many of both $v''$ and $v'$ progressions are observed. Table 4–2 illustrates the type of data available from an electronic emission spectrum. It can be seen that $v''$ progressions are tabulated in vertical columns, and $v'$ progressions in horizontal rows of figures. Therefore, first and second differences on the vertical columns of figures enable one to calculate $\omega'_e$ and $\omega_e x'_e$, whereas $\omega''_e$ and $\omega_e x''_e$ are obtainable from first and second differences on the horizontal rows. This form of table was originally deduced by Deslandres, whose studies began in 1885.

For high-resolution spectra, the determination of the values of $\bar{\nu}_{00}$ can, in principle, be carried out readily. However, if a high-resolution spectrograph is not available, we must use band-head data, which is less precise than band-origin data for a vibrational analysis.

So far we have not discussed how the assignment of appropriate $v'$ and $v''$ numbers to every observed band is carried out. If one contemplates Table 4–2, he can see in principle how the various progressions can be distinguished, even though they may overlap. Furthermore, in favorable cases, progressions tend to fade gradually with increasing $v$-number, but terminate abruptly at the band corresponding to either $v' = 0$ or $v'' = 0$. This often enables one to make the correct assignment of upper-and lower-state vibrational numbers to all observed bands. However, it is a method which sometimes requires considerable experience and art and is not always applicable. An unambiguous assignment can be made by studying the vibrational isotope effect.

### VIBRATIONAL ISOTOPE EFFECT

The shape of the Morse curve, which we have described, is determined by electronic factors, namely, the mutual attractions and repulsions of electrons and nuclei. Therefore, if an isotopic substitution is made, the electronic factors are unaffected, so the Morse curve is unchanged. The change in mass will, however, affect properties of the molecule in which mass is involved, which includes vibrational energy.

From the equation for the vibration of a diatomic molecule which obeys simple harmonic motion,

$$\nu_{\text{vib}} = \frac{1}{2\pi} \sqrt{\frac{k}{\mu}}, \tag{3–19}$$

it can be seen that the greater the reduced mass, the lower the vibrational frequency, and hence, since $\omega_e = \nu_{\text{vib}}/c$, the more closely spaced will be the vibrational levels. If the isotopic species is indicated by the superscript $i$, it follows from Eq. (3–19) that

$$\frac{\nu^i_{\text{vib}}}{\nu_{\text{vib}}} = \sqrt{\frac{\mu}{\mu^i}} = \rho, \tag{4–11}$$

where $\rho$ is introduced as shorthand notation for $\sqrt{\mu/\mu_i}$. Therefore

$$\nu^i_{\text{vib}} = \rho\nu_{\text{vib}} \quad \text{and} \quad \omega^i_e = \rho\omega_e. \tag{4-12}$$

Hence the energy spacing of isotopic harmonic vibrational levels is given by

$$G(v)^i = \rho\omega_e(v + \tfrac{1}{2}). \tag{4-13}$$

This equation is quite adequate to predict vibrational isotope shifts provided that $v$ is not large.

To correct precisely for anharmonic effects, the following equation should be used

$$G(v)^i = \rho\omega_e(v + \tfrac{1}{2}) + \rho^2\omega_e x_e(v + \tfrac{1}{2})^2. \tag{4-14}$$

Equation (4–10) can be rewritten in the form

$$\bar{\nu}_{00} = T_e + G(v') - G(v''), \tag{4-15}$$

and it follows for the isotopic species that

$$\bar{\nu}^i_{00} = T_e + G(v')^i - G(v'')^i. \tag{4-16}$$

Therefore, the isotope shifts observed in band-origin data are given by the difference between Eqs. (4–15) and (4–16):

$$\nu_{00} - \bar{\nu}^i_{00} = G(v') - G(v')^i - G(v'') + G(v'')^i. \tag{4-17}$$

Many elements, such as chlorine and bromine, are mixtures of abundant isotopes (cf. Table 4–3), so that the isotope effect is essentially "built-in," and is readily observed. Table 4–3 shows how observed experimental data can be matched with calculations based on Eqs. (4–14) through (4–17). Greater precision might be expected in this example if band-origin data were available.

**Table 4–3**

VIBRATIONAL ISOTOPE SHIFTS OF
NBr-BANDS $(\text{cm}^{-1})$, BASED ON $NBr^{79}$ AND $NBr^{81}$*

| $v' - v''$ | Calculated | Observed from band heads |
|:---:|:---:|:---:|
| 7–6 | 2.427 | 2.41 |
| 8–7 | 2.592 | 2.58 |
| 8–6 | 3.622 | 3.61 |
| 9–7 | 3.754 | 3.75 |
| 8–5 | 4.687 | 4.68 |
| 9–6 | 4.784 | 4.78 |

* From Milton, Dunford and Douglas, *J. Chem. Phys.* **35,** 1202 (1961).

## PROBLEMS

1. The dissociation energy of a ground electronic state molecule, AB, is 78.0 kcal/mole. Its first electronically excited state is known to dissociate into one ground state atom and one excited atom. The energy of excitation of the excited atom is 50.0 kcal/mole. What is the maximum wavelength of light which will cause dissociation to occur? Assume that zero-point energies can be ignored. The difference in potential-energy minima for the two molecular states is 29,500 cm$^{-1}$. What is the bond dissociation energy of the excited state of AB in kcal/mole?

2. The onset of an absorption continuum in the spectrum of $I_2$ occurs at 4995Å. One ground-state atom and one excited atom correlate with the upper-state molecular potential-energy curve. The energy of excitation of the atom is 21.70 kcal/mole.

   a) Calculate $D_e$ for the ground state of molecular iodine in kcal/mole. Ignore the zero-point energy.

   b) The difference in energy between the minima of the two potential-energy curves is 43.13 kcal/mole. What is $D_e$ for the upper state of $I_2$?

3. The zero-point energy of the ground state of $N_2$ is 1176 cm$^{-1}$, and that of its lowest excited state is 727 cm$^{-1}$. The energy difference, $T_e$, between the minima of the two potential-energy curves is 50,206 cm$^{-1}$. What is the energy of the $(v' = 0) \rightarrow (v'' = 0)$ transition, in cm$^{-1}$? What is the corresponding wavelength?

4. The values of $\omega_e$ and $\omega_e x_e$ for upper and lower states of CO are 1515.61, 17.25 and 2170.21, 13.46 cm$^{-1}$, respectively. The $(0, 0)$-transition is observed at 64,746.55 cm$^{-1}$. Calculate the value of $T_e$.

5. The values of $\omega_e$ and $\omega_e x_e$ are 1580.36 and 12.073 cm$^{-1}$, respectively, for the ground state of molecular oxygen. Calculate its zero-point energy.

6. The dissociation energy of ground-state oxygen is 5.178 eV. Combine this with data of the previous problem to plot the Morse curve for oxygen. Show the spacing of vibrational levels on the graph.

7. For the ground state of hydrogen,

$$D_e = 38{,}278 \text{ cm}^{-1}, \qquad \omega_e = 4395.24, \qquad \text{and} \qquad \omega_e x_e = 118.00 \text{ cm}^{-1}.$$

   Repeat Problem 6 for $H_2$. Note the difference in vibrational spacing for $O_2$ and $H_2$.

8. Use a different color to show the vibrational spacings of $D_2$ on the Morse plot for $H_2$. Assume that $\omega_e$, $\omega_e x_e$ are 3118.46, 64.10 cm$^{-1}$, respectively, for $D_2$. Is it correct to use the same potential-energy curves for $H_2$ and $D_2$? Why?

9. A standard source for ultraviolet light is the hydrogen lamp, in which the hydrogen, excited by electron bombardment, radiates to the repulsive potential-energy curve associated with ground-state hydrogen atoms. Is the resultant radiation discrete or continuous? Why?

10. Use the band-origin data in Table 4–2 to obtain $\omega_e$ and $\omega_e x_e$ for both upper and lower electronic states. Calculate $T_e$ precisely.

11. Analyze the following band-origin data to obtain $\omega_e$ and $\omega_e x_e$ for both upper and lower states, $T_e$.

Electronic Band-Origin Data ($cm^{-1}$)

| $v'$ \ $v''$ | 0 | 1 | 2 | 3 |
|---|---|---|---|---|
| 0 | 24,699 | 23,123 | 21,571 | 20,043 |
| 1 | 25,667 | 24,091 | 22,539 | 21,011 |
| 2 | 26,603 | 25,027 | 23,475 | 21,947 |
| 3 | 27,507 | 25,931 | 24,379 | 22,851 |
| 4 | | 26,803 | 25,251 | 23,723 |
| 5 | | | 26,091 | 24,563 |
| 6 | | | | 25,371 |

12. The $5' \leftarrow 0''$ transition in $HCl^{35}$ occurs at 91,022 $cm^{-1}$. Calculate the position of the band origin for the same transition for $DCl^{35}$ on the basis that in both electronic states the molecule behaves as a harmonic oscillator. Assume that $\omega_e' = 2710$ and $\omega_e'' = 2990$ $cm^{-1}$ for $HCl^{35}$. What is $T_e$, the energy difference between potential-energy minima for the two electronic states, of both isotopic species?

13. The origin of the $(v' = 0) \rightarrow (v'' = 6)$ band in an electronic transition, observed in $N_2^{14}$, is located at 35,600 $cm^{-1}$. Given that $\omega_e' = 1460$ and $\omega_e'' = 2360$ $cm^{-1}$ for $N_2^{14}$, and based on the assumption that the harmonic approximation is adequate, calculate $T_e$, and the position of the corresponding band origin for $N^{14}N^{15}$.

14. It is suspected that an observed sequence of electronic bands involves the $5' \leftarrow 4''$, $4' \leftarrow 3''$, $3' \leftarrow 2''$, $2' \leftarrow 1''$, and $1' \leftarrow 0''$ transition in $C^{12}O^{16}$. Band origins are located at 63,399; 64,118; 64,829; 65,532; and 66,229 $cm^{-1}$; respectively. On the basis of the above assignment, predict the corresponding band origins for $C^{12}O^{18}$. Assume that $\omega_e' = 1516$, $\omega_e' x_e' = 17.25$, $\omega_e'' = 2170$, and $\omega_e'' x_e'' = 13.46$ $cm^{-1}$ for $C^{12}O^{16}$.

15. The $3'-0''$ transition in the Lyman series of $H_2$ occurs in the vacuum u.v. region. The following lines were assigned upon band analysis:

| | | | |
|---|---|---|---|
| $P(1)$ | 93,908.26 | $R(0)$ | 94,058.57 |
| $P(2)$ | 93,702.69 | $R(1)$ | 94,003.30 |
| $P(3)$ | 93,410.17 | $R(2)$ | 93,861.08 |
| $P(4)$ | 93,030.70 | $R(3)$ | 93,631.92 |
| $P(5)$ | 92,564.29 | $R(4)$ | 93,315.81 |
| $P(6)$ | 92,010.92 | $R(5)$ | 92,912.75 |
| $P(7)$ | 81,370.61 | $R(6)$ | 92,422.74 |
| $P(8)$ | 90,643.35 | $R(7)$ | 91,845.79 |
| $P(9)$ | 89,829.15 | $R(8)$ | 91,181.89 |

Obtain the rotational constants, $B_3'$ and $B_0''$; hence $r_3'$ and $r_0''$; and also the position of the zero line.

16. The following lines were observed in the $4' - 0''$ band of the Lyman series of $H_2$:

| | |
|---|---|
| 95,253.64 | 94,060.10 |
| 95,193.60 | 93,737.88 |
| 95,105.72 | 93,553.38 |
| 95,044.22 | 93,172.58 |
| 94,897.76 | 92,957.34 |
| 94,805.51 | 92,517.96 |
| 94,600.47 | 92,271.96 |
| 94,477.47 | 91,773.99 |
| 94,213.84 | |

Determine $B'_4$, $B''_0$, and the null gap.

17. Given that $B_v = B_e - \alpha_e(v + \frac{1}{2})$, where the subscript $e$ refers to values at the equilibrium internuclear distance, from the results of the previous two problems, determine $B_e$, $\alpha_e$, and $r_e$ for the upper state of $H_2$ in the Lyman series.

18. $Cl_2^{35}$ has a low-energy triplet, one component of which behaves like a $^1\Sigma$-state, so that the observed transitions from the ground state obey the usual rules for $P$- and $R$-branches. The following data in $cm^{-1}$ apply to the 0–0 band. Analyze for $B'_0$, $B''_0$, $r'_0$, $r''_0$, in $cm^{-1}$ and the null gap in $cm^{-1}$, Å.

| | |
|---|---|
| 18,147.85 | 18,145.02 |
| 7.81 | 4.41 |
| 7.71 | 3.94 |
| 7.60 | 3.23 |
| 7.22 | 2.69 |
| 6.91 | 1.87 |
| 6.66 | 0.34 |
| 6.25 | 38.64 |
| 5.93 | 36.76 |
| 5.42 | 34.71 |

# BOND-DISSOCIATION ENERGIES

In the previous chapter, one example was described briefly of how a bond-dissociation energy of an excited electronic state could be determined from spectroscopic data. It is the purpose of the present chapter to describe more fully the precise meaning of the term bond-dissociation energy, to give further examples of determinations of bond-dissociation energies from spectroscopic data, and to correlate spectroscopic results with those obtained from thermo-chemistry.

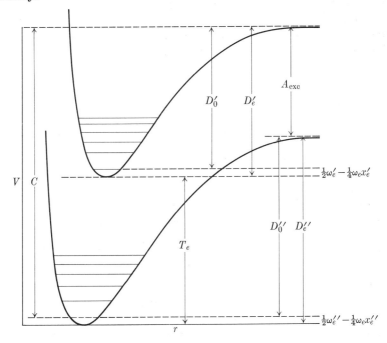

**Fig. 5-1.** Detailed illustration of data pertinent to the determination of bond-dissociation energies, $D$. The difference between $D_0$ and $D_e$ is the zero-point energy of the molecule. Here, $A_{\text{exc}}$ is the electronic energy of excitation of the atom(s) which correlate with the upper molecular electronic state; $C$ is the energy corresponding to the onset of an absorption continuum, $T_e$ is the electronic energy of excitation of the upper molecular electronic state.

## BOND-DISSOCIATION ENERGIES FROM ABSORPTION CONTINUA

Figure 5–1 illustrates in detail the parameters required to determine bond-dissociation energies from absorption spectroscopy. The onset of the continuum, $C$, corresponds to the energy required to excite a molecule from the $v = 0$ level of the electronic ground state to the dissociation limit of the excited electronic state. In order to obtain $D'_e$, the energy difference between the minimum and asymptote of the upper state curve, it is necessary to subtract $T_e$ and add $\frac{1}{2}\omega''_e - \frac{1}{4}\omega_e x''_e$ to $C$. Here $T_e$ is the difference in energies between the minima of the potential-energy curves of two electronic states, and $\frac{1}{2}\omega''_e - \frac{1}{4}\omega_e x''_e$ is the zero-point energy of the electronic ground state. These quantities are available from analysis of the absorption spectrum. A different and somewhat more practical way to define a bond-dissociation energy is in terms of $D_0$, rather than $D_e$. It can be seen from Fig. 5–1 that $D'_0$ is the energy difference between the $v' = 0$ level and the asymptote of the upper electronic state. Therefore $D'_0 < D'_e$, and the difference is the zero-point energy of the upper electronic state.

To obtain $D''_0$ one must subtract from $C$ the energy of excitation of one (or both) atoms associated with the upper electronic state of the molecule, $A_{\text{exc}}$. Energies of electronic excitation of atoms are known precisely from atomic spectroscopy. For the lower electronic state of the molecule a relationship between $D_e$ and $D_0$, analogous to that for the upper state, applies:

$$D''_e = D''_0 + \frac{1}{2}\omega''_e - \frac{1}{4}\omega_e x''_e. \tag{5–1}$$

## BOND-DISSOCIATION ENERGIES FROM EMISSION CONTINUA

An example of the elucidation of the bond-dissociation energy of a ground-state molecule from the onset of the continuum in an emission spectrum is illustrated in Fig. 5–2. The calculation here is essentially the reverse of that described above for an absorption spectrum, although the observed spectrum is usually much more complicated because of the fact that many band progressions are observed. For any given $v'$-progression, that is, a series of bands originating from a common upper-state vibrational level, the lower the energy of a given band head, the higher must be the quantum number of the ground electronic state vibrational level. Thus, if the onset of a continuum is observed at the end of a progression, it appears as a function of *decreasing* energy. It is possible, then, to observe many continua, each of which belongs to a different $v'$-progression. Provided that these progressions have been correctly labeled and the appropriate spectroscopic constants have been determined, it is possible to obtain the bond-dissociation energy of the ground-state molecule with equal accuracy from any $v'$-progression where the continuum is observed. Fig. 5–2 illustrates schematically the continuum, $C$, and some of the discrete transitions for the $v' = 9$ progression only. Also shown are the other quantities

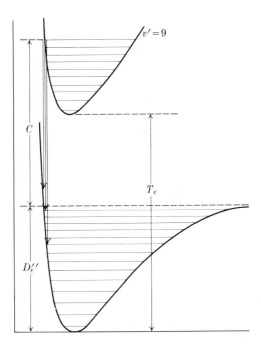

**Fig. 5-2.** The determination of $D_e''$ from onset of an emission continuum for the $v' = 9$ progression.

necessary to obtain the bond-dissociation energy of the electronic ground state. It is apparent from the diagram that the bond dissociation energy, $D_e''$, is equal to $T_e$ plus the energy required to excite the ninth vibrational level of the upper state, $G(9') = 9.5\ \omega_e' - 90.25\ \omega_e x_e'$, minus $C$, the maximum energy at which an emission continuum is observed.

### BOND-DISSOCIATION ENERGIES FROM PREDISSOCIATIONS

We have described earlier how molecules which have sufficient energy imparted to them will fly apart into their component atoms by traveling through the potential-energy well and out along the asymptote. Such a process is called *dissociation*. There is a similar process where the end result is the same, namely complete separation of the atoms, but where the mechanism, or pathway, is different. This process is called *predissociation*, which is now briefly described.

Cases are encountered, particularly for molecules composed of multivalent atoms and for polyatomic molecules, where potential-energy curves of different electronic states cross each other. Such a case is illustrated in Fig. 5-3, which shows a shallow quintet state of molecular nitrogen crossing a triplet and singlet state of nitrogen. (For our purposes at present, the spec-

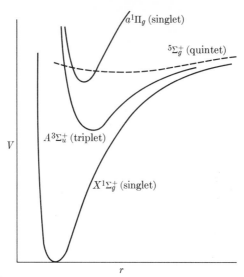

**Fig. 5-3.** Potential-energy diagram for some electronic states of $N_2$.

troscopic designations are for identification of states only.) It is readily possible to imagine that molecules which are oscillating in the upper singlet-state potential-energy well might be able to "leak" out along the quintet shallow well, and, with a small amount of kinetic energy, escape from the latter well and dissociate. Such a process does in fact occur, and is called predissociation. The rate at which it occurs is enhanced by collisions with other molecules, which facilitate the necessary changes in electronic configuration. When the rate of leakage is controlled solely by collisions, the process is called an *induced predissociation*.

Spectra involving an electronic state in which the potential-energy well is crossed by another potential-energy curve have unusual properties. The rotational fine structure in the region of the crossing point becomes diffuse and often disappears entirely at the crossing point. The same considerations may apply to entire bands observed under lower resolution. From these types of observations it was possible to deduce that the potential energy well of the quintet state of nitrogen does indeed have a shallow minimum. It is possible to show that the quintet state correlates with ground-state atomic nitrogen; that is, dissociation from the quintet molecular state, as from the molecular ground state, produces atoms in their ground state. Therefore the quintet-curve asymptote must coincide with the asymptote of the electronic ground state of $N_2$. It thus was possible to deduce the bond-dissociation energy of nitrogen as 9.756 eV, a quantity which had eluded determination by many other types of experiment. Similar considerations have been used to determine the bond-dissociation energy of the molecule HNO into H + NO; the appropriate potential-energy curves are represented schematically in Fig. 5-4.

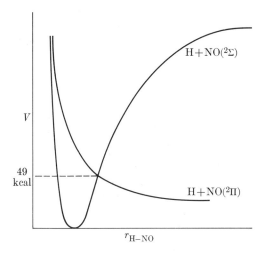

$r_{\text{H-NO}}$

**Fig. 5-4.** The potential-energy curves which govern the dissociation of HNO into H + NO. The H-NO bond dissociation requires 49 kcal/mole of energy. From Bancroft, Hollas and Ramsay, *Can. J. Phys.* **40**, 322 (1962).

### CORRELATION OF SPECTROSCOPIC AND THERMOCHEMICAL DATA

It is sometimes possible to obtain bond-dissociation energies directly from thermochemical measurements. Thus, for example, from a study of the change in pressure as a function of temperature in a heated quartz bulb containing iodine vapor, it is possible to deduce the dissociation energy of iodine by attributing the major apparent deviations from the ideal gas law to the dissociation reaction

$$I_2 \rightleftarrows 2I. \tag{5-2}$$

The equilibrium constant for the above reaction can be written as

$$K = \frac{[I]^2}{[I_2]}, \tag{5-3}$$

and both concentrations are readily deduced from the ideal gas law, the total amount of iodine present, and Dalton's law of partial pressures. A plot of $\log_{10} K$ vs. $1/T$ then yields $\Delta H°$, the heat of dissociation of one mole of molecular iodine vapor into two moles of atomic iodine (the slope of the plot = $-\Delta H°/2.30R$). There are two corrections which must be applied to $\Delta H°$, however, before this quantity can be directly compared to $D_0$. These two corrections tend to cancel, but total cancellation would be fortuitous. The first correction is necessary because $D_0$ refers to the bond-dissociation energy of molecules in the $v = 0$ level only, whereas in the thermochemical work carried out at elevated temperatures, many iodine molecules would populate levels where $v > 0$. The population of vibrational levels by the iodine molecules follows a Boltzmann-type of distribution function. The most readily derived Boltzmann function is the barometric pressure formula, $p = p_0 e^{-mgh/kT}$. The equation of interest here is completely analogous (except that we are concerned with a distribution among quantum levels, and not a continuous energy distribution):

$$n_i = g_i n_0 e^{-\epsilon_i/kT}, \tag{5-4}$$

where $n_i$ is the number of molecules in the $i$th energy level of energy $\epsilon_i$; $n_0$ is the number in the 0th energy level; $k$ is the Boltzmann constant, obtained by dividing the molar gas constant, $R$, by Avogadro's number, $N$; $T$ is the absolute temperature; and $g_i$ is a statistical weight factor, which differs from unity when there are degenerate energy levels, that is, more than one level of a given energy. For the particular case of vibrational energy, $i$ is replaced by $v$, the vibrational quantum number; $g_v = 1$ for all vibrational levels; and $\epsilon_v$ in ergs (see Eq. 3-25) is given by

$$\epsilon_v = [\omega_e(v + \tfrac{1}{2}) - \omega_e x_e(v + \tfrac{1}{2})^2]hc. \tag{5-5}$$

Therefore the ratio of the number $n$ of iodine molecules in the first vibrational level $v_1$ to those in the level $v = 0$ is given by

$$n_1/n_0 = e^{-(\omega_e - 2\omega_e x_e)hc/kT}. \tag{5-6}$$

The quantity $(\omega_e - 2\omega_e x_e)hc$ is the energy difference between the first two vibrational levels, $v = 0$ and $v = 1$, obtained from Eq. (5-5). The zero-point energy must be subtracted so that energies can be measured relative to the energy of the $v = 0$ level. Similarly, the ratios of populations occupying the $v = 2$ and $v = 0$ levels is given by

$$n_2/n_0 = e^{-(2\omega_e - 6\omega_e x_e)hc/kT}, \tag{5-7}$$

and so on. Because of the Boltzmann distribution, the population of the $v = 0$ level will be greatest and the population of higher-vibrational levels will decrease exponentially with increasing $v$. It is possible at any given temperature to deduce the distribution of iodine molecules among the various vibrational levels (see Fig. 5-5). The value of $\Delta H^\circ$ obtained from the negative slope of a plot of $\log_{10} K$ vs. $1/T$ therefore needs to be corrected for a vibrational distribution which changes as a function of temperature. Accurate values of $K$ as a function of temperature for the hypothetical equilibrium,

$$\text{I}_{2(v=0)} \rightleftarrows 2\text{I},$$

are required. Such data are not often computed and a widely used procedure is to ignore vibrational energy distribution entirely. This is clearly not a happy state of affairs. However, if precise values of $\log_{10} K$ are available over a limited temperature range where the vibrational population does not shift appreciably, a single term can be added to the value of $\Delta H^\circ$ to correct for the

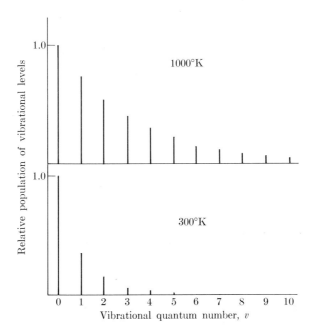

**Fig. 5-5.** Relative populations of vibrational levels of the iodine molecule, computed on the basis of a Boltzmann distribution, for room temperature and 1000°K.

effect of vibrational energy distribution. It should be noted that the higher the temperature and the heavier the molecule, the greater this correction will become.

The second correction, which must be applied to thermochemical bond-dissociation energies, is required to take into account the fact that prior to dissociation only one mole of particles exists, whereas after dissociation two moles of particles exist. Since all of these particles possess equal kinetic energy of translation, independent of their masses, the kinetic energy of translation is increased by a factor of two as a result of the dissociation process. This means that the observed absorption of heat is greater by the quantity $3/2 \, RT$ per mole of gas dissociated than that required simply to facilitate the dissociation process. Therefore the apparent dissociation energy is too large because of this correction, which provides some compensation for neglect of vibrational energy distribution.

Both of the above corrections are readily applied in precise fashion in the cases where thermochemical data are obtained at a single temperature, e.g., by direct calorimetry. The quantity $D_0$ can be seen from the above discussion to be a straightforward quantity. It is simply the energy difference between the $v = 0$ level and the asymptote of a given potential-energy curve, and is independent of vibrational and translational energy distributions and, hence, of temperature. Sometimes $D_0$ is designated $D_0^0$, since it really refers to the dissociation energy of molecules in the $v = 0$ level at $0°K$, where the translational energy is zero.

Thermochemical data applied to polyatomic molecules will only yield *average* bond energies. For example, from the standard heats of combustion of methane, the standard heats of formation of water and $CO_2$, the bond-dissociation energy of hydrogen, and the latent heat of sublimation of carbon (170 kcal/g-atom), it is possible to deduce, by the usual thermochemical manipulations, that the heat of the reaction

$$CH_4(g) \rightarrow C(g) + 4H(g)$$

is 398 kcal/mole of methane. This means that an *average* of 99.5 kcal must be supplied to break each mole of carbon–hydrogen bonds present. However, the quantity 99.5 kcal has no obvious relationship to the heats of any of the following reactions:

$$CH_4 \rightarrow CH_3 + H,$$
$$CH_3 \rightarrow CH_2 + H,$$
$$CH_2 \rightarrow CH\ + H,$$
$$CH\ \rightarrow C\ \ + H.$$

The heats of all of these reactions have been determined by an interesting variety of methods. For the first reaction, $\Delta H° = 102$ kcal/mole, as determined from reaction kinetic methods. The second reaction has $\Delta H° = 90$ kcal/mole, as determined from a combination of optical spectroscopy and mass spectrometry; and the last reaction has $\Delta H° = 80$ kcal/mole, obtained from spectroscopic measurements. Since the heats of all four reactions must total 398 kcal, then the heat of reaction $CH_2 \rightarrow CH + H$ must be 126 kcal/mole, in which the error is the cumulative total of errors on all other relevant determinations. Finally, it should be noted that thermochemical data are rarely precise to four significant figures, a precision readily obtained from pertinent optical spectral data.

## BOND-DISSOCIATION ENERGIES BY THE BIRGE-SPONER METHOD

The *a priori* calculation of simple harmonic force constants, at least with regard to relative values, has been performed with striking success from rather simple molecular orbital theory. However, neither simple harmonic force constants, $k$, nor harmonic vibration frequencies, $\nu = c\omega_e$, have any precise correlation with bond-dissociation energies; nor would a correlation be expected. The simple harmonic parabolic potential-energy well is a close approximation to the Morse curve only at the bottom of the well, where the vibration quantum number, $v$, approaches zero (cf. Fig. 4–1). On the other hand, the dissociation process involves a molecule excited to high vibrational levels in the region of the asymptote of the Morse curve, where the anharmonic contribution to the vibrational energy, $\omega_e x_e (v + \frac{1}{2})^2$, becomes appreciable compared to the harmonic contribution, $\omega_e(v + \frac{1}{2})$. The *a priori* calculation of the bond-dissociation energies of molecules is a tedious, involved, and complicated quantum-mechanical problem, which has been performed rigorously only for the hydrogen molecule. However, a simple procedure which takes into account the extent of anharmonicity of the molecular vibrations was developed by Birge and Sponer. Although the predicted bond-dissociation energies are usually approximately 15 percent too high, the relative correlation with experimental results is, in general, remarkably good.

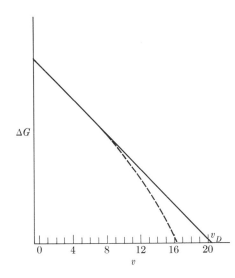

**Fig. 5–6.** The Birge-Sponer plot (solid line), used to determine the bond-dissociation energy, BDE. The BDE is effectively the area under the plot. It can also be computed from $v_D$, the vibrational level nearest the dissociation limit. The dashed line indicates typical observed behavior.

The energy of the $(v + 1)$ vibrational level is given by

$$G(v + 1) = \omega_e(v + \tfrac{3}{2}) - \omega_e x_e(v + \tfrac{3}{2})^2, \qquad (5\text{--}8)$$

whereas the energy of the $v$ level is

$$G(v) = \omega_e(v + \tfrac{1}{2}) - \omega_e x_e(v + \tfrac{1}{2})^2. \qquad (3\text{--}25)$$

Expansion of both equations, and subtraction of Eq. (3–25) from Eq. (5–8), leads to

$$\Delta G(v) = -2\omega_e x_e \cdot v + (\omega_e - 2\omega_e x_e). \qquad (5\text{--}9)$$

This equation, which gives an expression for the decrease in spacings between adjacent vibrational levels as a function of $v$, is of the same form as the general equation of a straight line, $y = mx + b$. It is clear that a plot of $\Delta G(v)$ vs. $v$ will be linear with a negative slope of $-2\omega_e x_e$ (cf. Fig. 5–6). When $\Delta G(v) = 0$, then $2\omega_e x_e \cdot v = \omega_e - 2\omega_e x_e$; in other words $v = \omega_e/2\omega_e x_e - 1$. The latter value of $v$ is finite, so the physical significance of $\Delta G(v) = 0$ must be that the dissociation limit of the molecule has been reached. The value of $v$ corresponding to the dissociation limit might be labeled $v_D$. Substitution of $v_D$ into Eq. (3–25) leads to the bond-dissociation energy of the molecule, $D_e$.

$$D_e = \omega_e(v_D + \tfrac{1}{2}) - \omega_e x_e(v_D + \tfrac{1}{2})^2 \tag{5-10}$$

$$= \omega_e\left(\frac{\omega_e}{2\omega_e x_e} - \frac{1}{2}\right) - \omega_e x_e\left(\frac{\omega_e}{2\omega_e x_e} - \frac{1}{2}\right)^2,$$

$$D_e = \frac{\omega_e^2}{4\omega_e x_e} - \frac{1}{4}\,\omega_e x_e, \tag{5-11}$$

$$D_e \simeq \frac{\omega_e{}^2}{4\omega_e x_e}. \tag{5-12}$$

The latter quantity is essentially the area under the straight line of Fig. 5–6. For molecules where the vibrational spacing has been determined precisely to high values of $v$, the actual plots of $\Delta G(v)$ vs. $v$ are of the form indicated by the dashed line of Fig. 5–6, so that observed bond-dissociation energies tend to be somewhat lower than those predicted by the Birge-Sponer method.

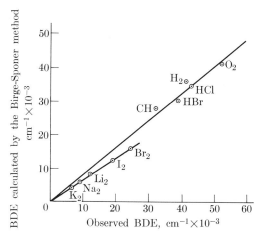

**Fig. 5–7.** Plots of bond-dissociation energies computed by the Birge-Sponer method vs. observed values of the bond-dissociation energies. The molecule $N_2$ adheres exactly to the uppermost plot, but is off the graph.

The method gives quite precise relative values, however, as shown in Fig. 5–7, and an empirical correction factor yields results in even closer agreement. The Birge-Sponer method is also of considerable merit in that it enables one to estimate $v$ at the dissociation limit. In addition, it emphasizes the importance of the anharmonicity of molecular vibrations near the dissociation limit.

**PROBLEMS**

1. A banded structure is observed in the absorption spectrum of oxygen, which changes to a continuum at a wavelength corresponding to 7.047 eV. The upper state of molecular oxygen dissociates into one ground state and one excited ($^1D$) atom. The excitation energy of the latter is 1.967 eV. Determine $D_0''$ for $O_2$ in kcal/mole.

2. The zero-point energy of the ground state of $O_2$ is 793 cm$^{-1}$, and the difference in energy between the potential-energy minima of the two electronic states, $T_e$, of Problem 5–1 is 49,800 cm$^{-1}$. Determine $D_e$ for the upper and ground states of $O_2$ in cm$^{-1}$.

3. From the analysis of an absorption spectrum of $Cl_2^{35}$, the following constants are obtained: $\omega_e' = 239.4$, $\omega_e x_e' = 5.4$, and $T_e = 18,310$ cm$^{-1}$. For the ground state, $\omega_e'' = 564.9$ and $\omega_e x_e'' = 4.0$ cm$^{-1}$. The convergence limit (position of onset of a continuum) occurs at 20,890 cm$^{-1}$. The upper electronic state of $Cl_2$ correlates with one ground-state atom and one excited atom. The excitation energy of the latter is 881 cm$^{-1}$. Determine $D_0$ and $D_e$ for both upper and lower states in cm$^{-1}$.

4. From spectroscopic measurements, $D_0 = 1.971$ and 4.476 eV for $Br_2$ and $H_2$, respectively. The molar heat of formation of $HBr(g)$ from the elements in their standard states is $-8.66$ kcal/mole (exothermic) at 300°K. The latent heat of evaporation of liquid bromine is $+7.34$ kcal/mole at 300°K. Assume that all molecules occupy the $v = 0$ level only, and determine $\Delta H°_{diss}$ for the reaction

$$HBr(g) \rightarrow H(g) + Br(g).$$

Also determine $D_0$ for HBr in kcal/mole. Why is there a difference between $\Delta H°_{diss}$ and $D_0$?

5. Given that $D_0 = 1.542$ and 4.476 eV for $I_2$ and $H_2$, respectively. Assume that all molecules occupy the $v = 0$ level at 300°K. From the following data determine $\Delta H°_{diss}$ and $D_0$ for HI at 300°K:

$$\tfrac{1}{2}H_2(g) + \tfrac{1}{2}I_2(s) = HI(g), \qquad \Delta H°_{300°K} = +6.20 \text{ kcal/mole};$$
$$I_2(s) = I_2(g), \qquad \Delta H°_{300°K} = +9.05 \text{ kcal/mole}.$$

6. The population of levels greater than $v = 0$ is appreciable for iodine molecules at 300°K. Given that $\omega_e = 215.0$, $\omega_e x_e = 0.61$ cm$^{-1}$, and that the population of levels greater than $v = 3$ can be neglected, determine:

   a) the relative populations of the first four vibrational levels,
   b) the average vibrational energy of $I_2$ at room temperature,
   c) the effect of the vibrational energy of $I_2$ on $\Delta H°$ for $HI(g) \rightarrow H(g) + I(g)$.

7. A plot of $\log_{10} K$ vs. $1/T$ for the equilibrium

$$S_2 \rightleftarrows 2S$$

has a negative slope of 22,900 degrees for the temperature range 4950–5050°K. The $S_2$-molecules behave effectively as though they populated the $v = 4$ level exclusively over this temperature range. From a band spectrum it is deduced that $\omega_e = 726$ and $\omega_e x_e = 2.8 \, \text{cm}^{-1}$ for ground electronic state $S_2$. Determine:

a) the difference in kinetic energy of the system for one mole of $S_2$ dissociated into atoms at 5000°K,

b) $\Delta H^{\circ}_{\text{diss}}$ at 5000°K,

c) $D_0$.

8. The values of $\omega_e''$ and $\omega_e x_e''$ are 691.75 and 4.720 $\text{cm}^{-1}$, respectively for the molecule NBr$^{79}$. From the Birge-Sponer method, estimate (a) the dissociation energy, and (b) the highest value of $v''$ before dissociation occurs.

9. Derive the Birge-Sponer expression for (a) $v_D$, the vibrational level corresponding to the dissociation limit of a molecule, and (b) $D_e$, the bond-dissociation energy.

## CHAPTER 6

# ATOMIC ORBITALS

We shall be concerned in this chapter with a brief review of atomic orbital (a.o.) theory and some of the correlation between spectroscopic and a.o. terminology. This is required prior to a discussion of molecular orbital theory, which follows in the next chapter.

## THE HYDROGEN ATOM

From solutions of the Schrödinger wave equation for the hydrogen atom, it is possible to obtain distribution functions as to the probability of finding the electron at a given distance from the nucleus. These lead to the well-known cloud representations of the various electron distributions, which indicate that there is an uncertainty in the position of the electron; however, this uncertainty is finite within certain limits. Similarly, it is possible to obtain velocity distribution functions for the electron which complement the position distribution function, and show a similar uncertainty in velocity. Both position and velocity are described in terms of coordinates $x$, $y$, and $z$ or their equivalents, $r$, $\theta$, and $\phi$. If the latter coordinates are used, then the Schrödinger equation for the hydrogen atom can be factored into three components which are dependent only on $r$, $\theta$, or $\phi$, respectively. The simplest component, dependent only on $\phi$, can be expressed in terms of a function of $m_l$, which is called the magnetic quantum number for reasons which will be discussed below. Only integral values of $m_l$ are allowed:

$$m_l = 0, \pm 1, \pm 2, \ldots \tag{6-1}$$

The component of the Schrödinger equation which is dependent upon $\theta$ also includes $m_l$. Its solutions, obtained from associated Legendre polynomials, define the orbital (azimuthal) quantum number, $l$, which can have the values

$$l = 0, 1, 2, \ldots \tag{6-2}$$

Finally, the component of the Schrödinger equation dependent upon $r$, which also includes $l$, can be solved in terms of associated Laguerre polynomials to obtain the allowed values of $n$, the principal quantum number:

$$n = 1, 2, 3, \ldots \tag{6-3}$$

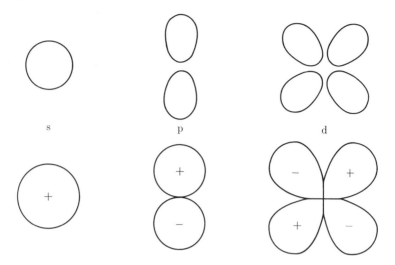

**Fig. 6-1.** Some types of atomic orbitals and electron distributions. The lower plots are of the wave functions $\psi$, and they show the shapes of s, p, and d atomic orbitals. The upper plots, of contour surfaces for $\psi^2$, represent the chance within limits, say 90 percent probability, that the electron is found within the boundaries shown for the electron clouds.

The allowed values of the quantum numbers are obtained in a natural way from the boundary conditions imposed on the wave equations. The three quantum numbers, defined above, are interdependent. Thus for any given value of $n$, $l$ can have any allowed value up to $(n-1)$, and for any given value of $l$, $m_l$ can have any integral value up to $\pm l$. For example, if $n = 2$, $l = 0$ and 1. For the case where $l = 0$, $m_l = 0$ only; for $l = 1$, $m_l$ can have any of the values $-1$, 0, 1.

The energy of the electron in a hydrogen atom is determined solely by the principal quantum number, $n$. If $n > 1$, then an excited state of the hydrogen atom must result. The orbital (or azimuthal) quantum number, $l$, determines the shape of the orbital occupied by the electrons. When $l = 0$, the electron occupies an s atomic orbital, when $l = 1$, a p atomic orbital, when $l = 2$, a d atomic orbital (see Fig. 6-1) and when $l = 3$, an f atomic orbital. We shall define the term *degenerate orbitals* to mean orbitals with the same value of $n$ and $l$. Degenerate orbitals have the same energy.* The number of allowed values of $m_l$, for any given value of $l$, is equal to the number of degenerate orbitals. Thus for $l = 1$, $m_l = -1$, 0, 1, and there are three degenerate

---

* For the hydrogen atom, all orbitals with the same values of $n$ have the same energy, but for multielectron atoms, only orbitals with the same value of both $n$ and $l$ have the same energy.

p-orbitals; for $l = 2$, $m_l = -2, -1, 0, 1, 2$, and there are five degenerate d-orbitals.

We are not concerned here with the mathematics involved in the solution of the Schrödinger equation, but there are certain features of the resultant wave function, $\psi$, which deserve our attention. The wave function for a single electron atom is

$$\psi_{nlm_l} = N_{nlm_l} \cdot R_{nl}(r) \cdot P_{lm_l}(\theta) \cdot M_{m_l}(\phi), \tag{6-4}$$

where the subscripts $n$, $l$, and $m_l$ indicate a dependence of the solutions on the values of the quantum numbers. Thus for one particular set of values of $n$, $l$, and $m_l$, the wave function $\psi$ describes the corresponding atomic orbital. In Eq. (6–4) $N$ is a normalizing factor such that the integral

$$N^2 \int \psi^2 \, d\tau = 1. \tag{6-5}$$

The probability of finding the electron in any given element of volume, $d\tau$, is proportional to $\psi^2$ for that element. The normalizing factor $N$ converts this relative probability to an absolute fractional probability, since when the integral is equal to one, the probability of finding the electron in all of space is equal to unity. Also in Eq. (6–4), $R(r)$ is a function which describes the dependence of $\psi$ on $r$, the distance between the nucleus and electron, and which includes associated Laguerre polynomials; $P(\theta)$ is a function which describes the dependence of $\psi$ on the angular coordinate $\theta$, and which includes associated Legendre polynomials. Finally, $M(\phi)$ describes the dependence of $\psi$ on the angle $\phi$. The general solution, $M(\phi)$, is of the form

$$M(\phi) = e^{im_l\phi}, \tag{6-6}$$

where $i = \sqrt{-1}$. This is the only factor in Eq. (6–4) which involves complex numbers and it merits further discussion. Let us first discuss the case where $l = 1$; hence $m_l = 1, 0, -1$. Equation (6–6) is reduced to

$$M(\phi) = 1, \tag{6-7}$$

when $m_l = 0$. When $m_l = 1$ and $-1$, then Eq. (6) becomes

$$M(\phi) = e^{i\phi}, \tag{6-8}$$

$$M(\phi) = e^{-i\phi}, \tag{6-9}$$

respectively. However, wave equations in quantum mechanics, as in classical mechanics, have an important practical property. This property is that linear combinations of solutions to a wave equation may also be solutions of the same wave equation. Thus by using the relations

$$e^{i\phi} = \cos \phi + i \sin \phi, \tag{6-10}$$

$$e^{-i\phi} = \cos \phi - i \sin \phi, \tag{6-11}$$

it is possible to show that alternatives to Eq. (6–6) are given by

$$M(\phi) = e^{i\phi} + e^{-i\phi}$$
$$= 2 \cos \phi, \tag{6-12}$$

$$M(\phi) = 1/i(e^{i\phi} - e^{-i\phi})$$
$$= 2 \sin \phi, \tag{6-13}$$

when $m_l = \pm 1$. For Eq. (6–13), the factor $1/i$ is included so that the solution is "real." Equations (6–7), (6–12), and (6–13) correspond to the $M(\phi)$ part of $\psi$ for $p_z$-, and $p_y$-orbitals, respectively. The energy of a single electron is identical whether it occupies a $p_x$-, $p_y$-, or $p_z$-orbital. Similarly, the shapes of the three orbitals are identical; they are given by the equations for three dimensional stationary waves. Only the orientation of the three orbitals in space is different. In a similar fashion to that outlined above, when $l = 2$, $m_l = 2$, 1, 0, −1, or −2, and the resultant stationary wave functions for the five d-orbitals are obtained. For $m_l = 0$, the function for $M(\phi)$ corresponds to the $d_{z^2}$-orbital. Two linear combinations of solutions for $M(\phi)$ corresponding to $m_l = \pm 1$ lead to $d_{xz}$- and $d_{yz}$-orbitals; and two linear combinations for $m_l = \pm 2$ yield $d_{x^2-y^2}$- and $d_{xy}$-orbitals.

So far we have not discussed the significance of Eqs. (6–8) and (6–9) and similar equations which provide "imaginary" solutions to $M(\phi)$. These "imaginary" solutions correspond to running waves, rather than stationary waves and are of practical importance in discussing the effect of a magnetic field on the energies of electrons (see the discussion of angular momentum that follows).

## ANGULAR MOMENTUM OF THE ELECTRON IN A HYDROGEN ATOM

The electron in a hydrogen atom moves in the radial electrostatic field of the nucleus. Such a central field can exert no moment of force or torque on the electron, so that its angular momentum is constant.* The orbital angular momentum of the electron can be represented by a vector **l** of magnitude $\hbar\sqrt{l(l+1)}$ (cf. the analogy with Eq. 2–10). The orbital angular-momentum vector originates at the nucleus and is at right angles to the cross section through the center of the electron cloud. When the electron cloud is spherically symmetric, as in an s-orbital, there is no net motion of the electron cloud *around* the nucleus; hence the vector **l** is not defined and the corresponding quantum number, $l$, is zero.† If $l = 1$, the electron occupies a p-orbital and has

---

* This is a consequence of Newton's second law. There is a quantum mechanical analog to the classical model.
† See W. Kauzmann, *Quantum Chemistry* (New York: Academic Press), 1957, pp. 221–4, for an interesting physical picture of the motion of an electron about a nucleus.

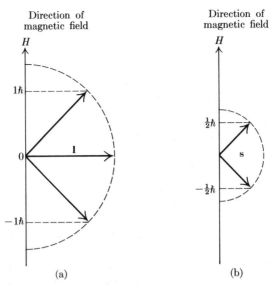

**Fig. 6-2.** The effect of a magnetic field on the orientations of angular-momentum vectors: (a) for $l$ of magnitude $\sqrt{2}\hbar$. The projections are of magnitude $\hbar$, 0, and $-\hbar$, and the corresponding values of $m_l$ are 1, 0, and $-1$. Part (b) illustrates the effect on s, which always has the magnitude $\sqrt{\frac{3}{4}}\hbar$. The projections are of magnitude $+\frac{1}{2}\hbar$ and $-\frac{1}{2}\hbar$ and the values of $m_s$ are $\pm\frac{1}{2}$. No interaction between l- and s-vectors was assumed, which is not rigorously correct. The interaction of l and s increases in the series H, Li, Na, K.

$\sqrt{2}\ \hbar$ units of orbital angular momentum. If $l = 2$, the electron occupies a d-orbital and has $\sqrt{6}\ \hbar$ units. Let us consider in more detail the case of an electron with $l = 1$.

Since the three p-orbitals are all equivalent in free space, it does not matter which orbital the electron occupies. However, as we have seen, there is some arbitrariness in the choice of mathematical description of the three orbitals. In the absence of a magnetic field, the orbital for the single electron in the hydrogen atom is described satisfactorily by any of three $\psi$-equations, which include $M(\phi)$, given by Eqs. (6–7), (6–12), or (6–13). Under the influence of an external magnetic field, $M(\phi)$ is given by Eqs. (6–7), (6–8), or (6–9). If we represent the magnetic field in the $z$-direction and the orbital angular momentum by the vector l, then in the absence of complicating effects due to electron spin, there are three allowed projections of this vector on the $z$-axis of magnitude 1, 0, and $-1$, in units of $\hbar$ (see Fig. 6–2a). The numbers 1, 0, and $-1$ are the allowed values of the magnetic quantum number, $m_l$, corresponding to Eqs. (6–8), (6–7), and (6–9); and the corresponding orbitals, $\psi$, are designated $p_1$, $p_0$ and $p_{-1}$, respectively. The $p_z$- and $p_0$-orbitals are identical, so that in the presence and absence of an external magnetic

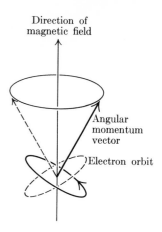

**Direction of magnetic field**

**Fig. 6–3.** The effect a magnetic field would have on the motion of an electron if it moved in a classical orbit in a plane not at right angles to an external magnetic field. The orbit wobbles around the direction of the magnetic field with a resultant precession motion of the angular-momentum vector, which is at right angles to the electron orbit.

field directed along the $z$-axis, the corresponding electron cloud does not rotate about the $z$-axis.*

However, the equations for the $p_1$- and $p_{-1}$-orbitals contain $M(\phi) = e^{i\phi}$ and $e^{-i\phi}$, respectively. These correspond to running waves, in which there is a net rotation of the electron cloud about the $z$-axis. We can illustrate the effect of the magnetic field by using a classical example. If the electron could be constrained in an elliptical orbit about the nucleus, then application of an external magnetic field in a direction not parallel to the axis of the orbit would cause the orbit to wobble about the direction of the magnetic field, as a spinning top which is not aligned with the earth's gravitational field will wobble. The motion of the corresponding angular-momentum vector is a precession about the direction of the magnetic field (Fig. 6–3). In reality, because of the uncertainty relation, nature does not permit a precise definition of the pathway of the electron. However, the frequency of precession of the angular-momentum vector is given by

$$\nu = He/4\pi m_e c, \tag{6–14}$$

where $H$ is the strength of the external magnetic field, $e$ and $m_e$ are the charge and mass of the electron, respectively, and $c$ is the velocity of light. The shift in energy levels of the electron that results from the magnetic field is given by $\epsilon = m_l h\nu$, where $m_l$ is the magnetic quantum number, not to be confused with $m_e$. Combination with Eq. (6–14) gives

$$\epsilon = m_l h \, He/4\pi m_e c. \tag{6–15}$$

Equation (6–15) can be rearranged to yield

$$\epsilon = B_M m_l H, \tag{6–16}$$

---

* The choice of the $z$-axis for the direction of the external magnetic field and the choice of which orbital shall be designated $p_z$, is arbitrary and is a choice of convenience only.

where $B_M$, called the Bohr magneton, is given by

$$B_M = eh/4\pi m_e c. \qquad (6\text{-}17)$$

The energy levels are thus equal to a constant, times the magnetic quantum number, times the strength of the magnetic field (Fig. 6–4). Thus the energies of the electrons in the orbitals are still sharply defined under the influence of the magnetic field, although the degeneracy of orbitals which have the same values of $n$ and $l$ is removed.

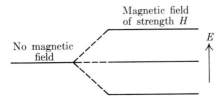

**Fig. 6–4.** Relative energies of electrons in p orbitals of hydrogen atoms in the absence and presence of an external magnetic field. Interaction of the electron spin with orbital motion is neglected.

The final quantum number is that for electron spin, $m_s$, which can have values of $\pm\frac{1}{2}$. The effect of the apparent spin of the electron shows up under the influence of a magnetic field. There is a spin angular-momentum vector, **s**, which is associated with the apparent spin; it is defined in terms of the quantum number, $s$. The only allowed value of this quantum number is $s = +\frac{1}{2}$. The magnitude of **s** is $\hbar\sqrt{s(s+1)} = \sqrt{\frac{3}{4}}\,\hbar$. Under the influence of a magnetic field the electron orients itself in one of two possible ways (see Fig. 6–2b), so that if orbital and spin angular momenta could be separated, there would be only two possible projections of **s** on the axis representing the direction of the field. These two projections are of magnitude $+\frac{1}{2}\hbar$ and $-\frac{1}{2}\hbar$, and the allowed values of $m_s$ are $+\frac{1}{2}$ and $-\frac{1}{2}$.* The two possible orientations of the electron are commonly designated ↑ and ↓ , which indicate the directions of the projections which define the values of $m_s$. Thus as the values of $m_l$ are obtained from projections of **l**, so the values of $m_s$ are obtained from projections of **s**.

The above discussion, in which orbital and spin angular momenta were treated independently, provides a picture of the behavior of hydrogen atoms in an external magnetic field which is adequate for our purposes; and it

---

* It is a consequence of the Heisenberg uncertainty principle that the projection of an angular-momentum vector on one axis is never as large as the vector itself. This is true whether one is discussing spin, orbital, or total angular momentum. If the projection were as large as the original vector, then the angular momentum would be zero in the direction of the other two axes, and so would be sharply defined in the direction of all three axes. Only the total angular momentum and angular momentum along any one arbitrarily chosen axis can be known with certainty.

illustrates how allowed values of the two quantum numbers, $m_l$ and $m_s$ can be deduced. However, the electron in a hydrogen atom does not need to be placed between the poles of an external magnet to feel the effects of a magnetic field; there is a magnetic field built into the hydrogen atom. Although the electron moves about the nucleus, so far as the electron is concerned, it seems to move as if it were inside an orbit of the nucleus, just as the sun appears to rotate about the earth. The rotation of the charged nucleus produces an electric current, and thus a magnetic field is formed which causes the spinning electron to align in one of the two possible ways. This alignment affects the total energy of the atom. Hence there is a spin-orbit interaction. It can be described vectorially by saying that the l- and s-vectors are coupled in two different ways to form two resultant j-vectors. The strength of the coupling is reflected in the speed of precession of l and s about the resultant j, and in the extent that energy levels corresponding to a given value of $l$ are split into two sublevels. The precession of l and s about one resultant j is illustrated in Fig. 6-5a. The rules for quantum vector addition will be outlined in detail later.

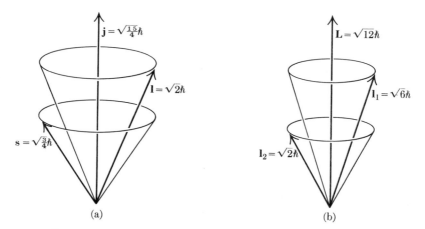

(a)                                    (b)

**Fig. 6-5.** Representations of the precession of component vectors about their resultant vector. The rate of precession is proportional to the energy of interaction of the components, that is, the strength of the coupling. For a strong coupling, the component vectors lose their significance, since they no longer describe the electron motion. (a) For $s = \frac{1}{2}$, $l = 1$, the corresponding vectors are of magnitude $s = \sqrt{\frac{3}{4}}\,\hbar$, $l = \sqrt{2}\,\hbar$, and there are two resultant vectors: $j = \sqrt{\frac{15}{4}}\,\hbar$, (shown above) and $j = \sqrt{\frac{3}{4}}\,\hbar$, corresponding to $j = \frac{3}{2}$ and $\frac{1}{2}$, respectively. Interactions of l and s are caused by weak magnetic interactions between the orbit and spin of an electron, which give rise to the fine structure of atomic spectra. (b) For $l_1 = 2$, $l_2 = 1$, the corresponding vectors are $l_1 = \sqrt{6}\hbar$, $l_2 = \sqrt{2}\hbar$, and the resultant vectors are $L = \sqrt{12}\hbar$ (shown above to a different scale than that used in part a), $L = \sqrt{6}\hbar$, and $L = \sqrt{2}\hbar$, corresponding to $L = 3, 2$, and 1. The interactions of the electron orbits are caused by strong electrostatic repulsions, a major factor in determining multiplet structures for atoms.

If $l = 0$, there is no magnetic field due to orbital motion and hence no spin-orbit coupling. If $l \neq 0$, then spin-orbit coupling can occur. It is very weak in hydrogen atoms and is barely detectable for the valence electron of lithium. It does cause a detectable split of energy levels in sodium, which are reflected in the observed spectra (cf. the familiar sodium D-line doublet). The spin-orbit interaction is therefore reponsible for the observed fine structure in atomic spectra. The reason for enhanced spin-orbit interaction with increased atomic weight will be discussed later.

## MULTIELECTRON ATOMS

For atoms other than hydrogen, the energies of the electrons are not determined solely by the principal quantum number, $n$. More than one electron is present, and electron–electron repulsions become important. Each single electron is now under the influence of a noncentral force field. The effective result is that electrons closer to the nucleus act as though they form a partial screen which shields the outer electrons somewhat from the influence of the nucleus. Because of the different shapes of the orbitals (Fig. 6–1), some electrons spend more time near the nucleus than others, and hence provide a more effective screen. Thus electrons in s-orbitals, on the average, are closer to the nucleus than electrons in p-orbitals with the same value of $n$, and they provide a partial screen for the p-electrons. Therefore the p-electrons are of higher energy than the s-electrons. The order of increasing energy of atomic orbitals is 1s < 2s < 2p < 3s < 3p < 4s < 3d < 4p, etc., where the numbers are the values of $n$. Note that the 3d-orbitals are of higher energy than the 4s-orbitals—a striking illustration of the screening effect discussed above.

In the elucidation of the electron configuration of any given atom in terms of its atomic orbitals, the building-up (*aufbau*) principle is used, which states that electrons will fill atomic orbitals of lowest energy first. The Pauli exclusion principle states that no two electrons in the same atom can have the same values for all four quantum numbers, $n$, $l$, $m_l$, and $m_s$. In other words, a maximum of two electrons can occupy any given atomic orbital, and then only if one electron has $m_s = +\frac{1}{2}$ and the other has $m = -\frac{1}{2}$. Why electrons with opposite spin can occupy the same orbital whereas those with the same spin cannot appears rather mysterious, since the direct spin-spin interactions are weak. We shall return to this mystery in Chapter 10.

Electrons exert great electrostatic repulsive forces on each other, independent of spin, and so tend to avoid each other as much as possible, a phenomenon which minimizes the energy of the system. The rules of the Pauli principle, with which the electrons are always in accord, help to *define* the extent of the repulsive forces, since they provide a limit to the number of electrons in a given orbital, and hence define the average electron distribution in the atom. The effect of the Pauli principle has sometimes been described as caused by Pauli forces, but this is a term to be used with caution. It might be taken to imply that the Pauli principle is responsible for repulsive forces. The repulsive forces are electrostatic in nature, whereas the Pauli principle is like a policeman directing traffic. It signals to each electron a traffic lane which is vacant or which contains only one other electron. This greatly minimizes the chance of a collision. Some collisions still occur. The electrons, unlike automobiles, always recover, although they may drive off in the wrong lane. Despite collisions, never more than two electrons occupy one lane.

Some special cases in which the total energy is minimized, are summarized in two of Hund's rules. The first rule, known as Hund's *multiplicity rule*, can be stated as follows: "For equivalent electrons (electrons with the same $n$ and $l$), the state with largest total spin is the state of lowest energy." If all the electrons have their spins oriented in the same direction, then they are directed by the Pauli policeman into separate orbitals; hence minimizing the repulsive forces and the energy of the system. The multiplicity is defined as $2S + 1$, where $S$ is a total spin quantum number, determined by the spins of all the electrons (see below). Maximum total spin and maximum multiplicity are terms which can be used interchangeably.

Hund's *angular momentum rule* says that for states with the same multiplicity, the one with largest total angular momentum is the one with minimum energy. If electrons rotate about the nucleus in the same direction, their orbital angular momenta enhance the total angular momentum of the atom; but if they rotate in opposite directions, their effects tend to cancel. It is much easier for the electrons to stay out of each other's way when they are going in the same direction; this minimizes the repulsive forces.

### RUSSELL-SAUNDERS AND *j-j* COUPLING

The electrostatic repulsions between electrons cause their orbits to be shifted continuously. This can be represented by the precession of angular-momentum vectors, which are located along the axes of the electron orbits, about a resultant total angular-momentum vector, L (Fig. 6–5b). For $i$ electrons in light atoms the dominant interaction is the coupling of the $l_i$ orbital angular-momentum vectors to form the resultant L, of magnitude $\hbar\sqrt{L(L + 1)}$, where $L$ is a total orbital angular momentum quantum number. Similarly, the $s_i$ spin angular-momentum vectors can be coupled together to form a resultant vector S, of magnitude $\hbar\sqrt{S(S + 1)}$.

Finally, L and S can be coupled, or added vectorially, to form a resultant vector J, which is defined in terms of the total angular-momentum quantum number $J$. The magnitude of J is $\hbar\sqrt{J(J + 1)}$. For light atoms the coupling of the $l_i$ to form L, and of the $s_i$ to form S, is strong. This means that different values of $L$ and $S$ represent states of considerably different energies.* Con-

---

* States of different multiplicity differ in energy but *not* because of strong magnetic interactions of electron spins (see Chapter 10).

versely, the coupling of **L** and **S** to form a resultant **J** is weak for light atoms, so that for given values of **L** and **S**, the allowed resultant values of **J** do not differ much in energy. The above type of coupling is called Russell-Saunders or $L$-$S$ coupling.

On the other hand, we have seen that there is a magnetic interaction of the orbital and spin angular momentum of a single electron, and that this interaction becomes stronger, the larger the atomic weight. The enhanced spin-orbit interaction with increased atomic weight can be discussed in terms of the partial shielding effects of all but one electron on the remaining electron or, more precisely, in terms of the effect of penetration of the one electron inside the remaining electron cloud. The electrostatic potential changes much more rapidly as a function of distance from the nucleus for a valence electron when it penetrates deep into the electron cloud. There is a resultant enhancement in the velocity of the electron and in the average magnetic field felt by the electron. The larger the number of electrons, the larger the enhancement of the magnetic field. The electrons responsible for shielding need not be only inner (core) electrons, but may also be in the valence shell. Thus the spin-orbit interaction is strong in halogens, with their large number of valence electrons.

If the spin-orbit interaction is greater than the orbit-orbit interactions, then the individual **l**- and **s**-vectors for each electron couple to form resultant **j**-vectors, which, in turn, couple to form a total **J** for the atom.

All light atoms, particularly those with few valence electrons, as a first approximation obey Russell-Saunders coupling, whereas the heavier halogens and atoms with a large total number of electrons approximate **j-j** coupling. We shall henceforth confine our discussion to atoms which approximate Russell-Saunders coupling, although there is nothing intrinsically more difficult in the treatment of **j-j** coupling; in fact, the two types of coupling can be correlated.

The rules for deducing the allowed values of the quantum numbers $L$, $S$, and $J$, particularly for an atom with a large number of electrons, may seem to be insurmountably difficult. Fortunately, there are many simplifying features to the problem. We have already seen that for a single-electron system, a simple correlation exists between orbital angular momentum and the type of atomic orbital. Furthermore, for a multielectron atom, closed shells do not make any contribution to the total orbital or spin angular momentum of the atom. A closed shell is spherically symmetric so its contribution to total orbital angular momentum is zero;* all of its electrons are paired, so that its contribution to total spin angular momentum is also zero. Therefore for a closed shell it follows that $L = 0$, $S = 0$, and hence $J = 0$. The same considerations also apply to subshells. Thus for two electrons in an s-orbital, $L = S = J = 0$. Similarly, if six electrons are in three equivalent p-orbitals, the resultant electron cloud is spherically symmetric, and the electrons in each orbital must have paired spins. Therefore we again see that

---

* The mathematical proof is known as Unsöld's theorem.

$L = S = J = 0$. The latter result also applies to ten electrons in five equivalent d-orbitals. Thus our problem is reduced to one involving subshells which are not completely filled with electrons.

When electrons are fed into a subshell, one can see that the allowed values of $L$, $S$, and $J$ will increase with an increasing number of electrons. However, the allowed values of $L$, $S$, and $J$ eventually must pass through a maximum and then decrease, since when all of the equivalent orbitals are filled with electrons, we have returned to the situation $L = S = J = 0$. Furthermore, the allowed value of $S$ is maximal when the equivalent orbitals are half-filled with electrons. For a half-filled subshell, the resultant electron cloud is spherically symmetric, so one might anticipate correctly that the resultant total orbital angular momentum is zero. It has been clearly established that vacancies in a subshell which is more than half-filled are equivalent to electrons in a subshell which is less than half-filled, so far as the determination of the values of $L$ and $S$ is concerned. This means that a $p^5$-configuration has the same spectroscopic designation as a $p^1$-configuration, and a $p^4$-configuration is equivalent to $p^2$. (The superscripts indicate the number of electrons occupying equivalent p-orbitals.) This symmetry of "holes" and electrons is necessary in order to return to complete spherical symmetry when an additional subshell is filled.


### ENERGY LEVELS FOR PARTIALLY FILLED SUBSHELLS

Let us now consider in greater detail the properties of partially filled (open) subshells.* The electrons in the partially filled subshells have a strong tendency to avoid each other, a tendency caused by large electrostatic repulsions. Furthermore, because the electrons are indistinguishable, all possible permutations in their distribution must be considered. Finally, the spin interactions, resulting from the Pauli principle, must be taken into account. The result is a series of energy levels, known as the *multiplet structure*, for each electron configuration. For example, there are three different energy levels in the multiplet structure of a $p^3$-configuration, each of which is assigned its own spectroscopic term. Superimposed on the multiplet structure are closely spaced energy levels caused by the effect of spin-orbit interaction. The effect of these closely spaced levels on the observed atomic spectra is known as the *fine structure*. We shall consider several different ways of arriving at a correct total number of energy levels in a multiplet structure, but we shall neglect until later the effect of the weak spin-orbit interactions. Each of these methods has its own particular advantages and limitations.

First, let us consider the case of nonequivalent electrons, that is, electrons which do not have the same values of the quantum numbers $n$ and $l$.

---

* The effects of completed inner shells, the core electrons, can be neglected except for their enhancement of the spin-orbit interactions.

**Two nonequivalent electrons.** Let $l_1$ and $s_1$ be the orbital and spin quantum numbers of the first electron, and $l_2$ and $s_2$ be the corresponding quantum numbers of the second electron. The total orbital angular momentum quantum number, $L$, can be obtained from

$$L = (l_1 + l_2), (l_1 + l_2 - 1), \ldots (l_1 - l_2), \qquad (6\text{--}18)$$

where $l_1 \geq l_2$. Since $s_1 = s_2 = \frac{1}{2}$, it follows that the analog of Eq. (6–18) for spin angular momentum is

$$S = (s_1 + s_2), (s_1 - s_2) = 1, 0. \qquad (6\text{--}19)$$

The general rule used to obtain the allowed values of $J$ for a given $L$ and $S$ is

$$J = (L + S), (L + S - 1), \ldots (L - S), \qquad (6\text{--}20)$$

when $L \geq S$. Equation (6–20) applies to an atom containing any number of electrons. For $L \geq S$, there are $2S + 1$ values for $J$, and regardless of the relative values of $L$ and $S$, the quantity $2S + 1$ is called the multiplicity of the atomic state.*

**More than two nonequivalent electrons; vector addition.** Equations (6–18) and (6–19) summarize the rules for obtaining the quantum numbers $L$ and $S$ for two nonequivalent electrons. They summarize the correct values of $L$ and $S$, which can also be obtained by quantum vector addition. For more than two nonequivalent electrons, the simplest procedure to obtain allowed values of $L$ and $S$ is by quantum vector addition. The rules for quantum vector addition are the same as the rules for normal vector addition, to the extent that the parallelogram of forces is applicable, but there are additional restrictions. If all the quantum numbers corresponding to the component vectors have integral values (as for $l_i$, $L$, and perhaps $S$ and $J$), then the allowed values of the resultant quantum numbers must also be integers. If the vector addition involves an odd number of vectors corresponding to half-integral quantum numbers, the resultant quantum numbers must also be half integers; if an even number of half-integral quantum numbers are involved, the resultant quantum numbers are integers.

Consider the following examples. We shall start with addition of two vectors only. If there are two electrons, with $l_1 = 2$ and $l_2 = 1$, then the corresponding magnitudes of $\mathbf{l}_1$ and $\mathbf{l}_2$ are $\sqrt{6}\,\hbar$ and $\sqrt{2}\,\hbar$, respectively. Vector addition results in magnitudes of $\mathbf{L}$ equal to $\sqrt{12}\,\hbar$, $\sqrt{6}\,\hbar$, and $\sqrt{2}\,\hbar$ (Figs. 6–5b and 6–6). It can be seen that the component and resultant vectors

---

* It follows that when $S > L$, there are $2L + 1$ values of $J$, since negative values of $J$ are not allowed. The multiplicity, $2S + 1$, is nevertheless a fundamental quantity, even though not all atomic states can realize their full multiplicity. Atoms with the same values of $S$ have certain properties in common.

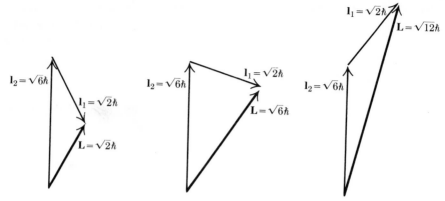

**Fig. 6–6.** Quantum addition of vectors $l_1 = \sqrt{2}\hbar$, $l_2 = \sqrt{6}\hbar$ to give resultant values of **L**. Since $l_1 = \sqrt{l_1(l_1 + 1)}\hbar$ and $\mathbf{L} = \sqrt{L(L + 1)}\hbar$, $l_1 = 1$, $l_2 = 2$, and the resultant allowed values of $L$ are 1, 2, and 3.

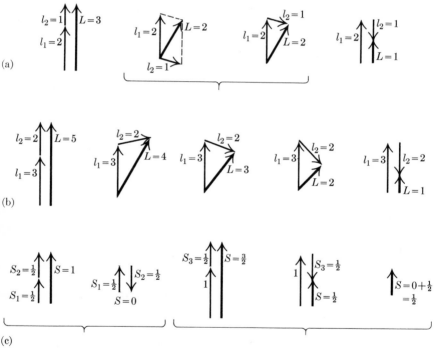

**Fig. 6–7.** Examples of simplified quantum vector addition. All vectors are directly proportional to the corresponding quantum numbers. (a) $l_1 = 2$, $l_2 = 1$, $L = 3$, 2, 1. The value of $L = 2$ is arrived at using the parallelogram of forces represented in two equivalent ways. (b) $l_1 = 3$, $l_2 = 2$, $L = 5$, 4, 3, 2, 1. (c) Addition of vectors corresponding to $S_1 = S_2 = S_3 = \frac{1}{2}$. First addition of $S_1$ and $S_2$ to obtain $S = 1$ or 0. Then addition of $S_3 = \frac{1}{2}$ to the resultant to obtain $S = \frac{3}{2}, \frac{1}{2}, \frac{1}{2}$.

cannot be parallel.* However, vectors whose magnitudes are defined in terms of square roots are cumbersome to add. For our purposes it is much simpler to use schematic vectors, the lengths of which are in direct proportion to the appropriate quantum numbers. So long as the rules for resultant integral or half-integral quantum numbers, outlined in the previous paragraph, are followed, then the correct results are obtained. Results for $l_1 = 2$, $l_2 = 1$ are illustrated using this simplified approach in Fig. 6–7(a). If $l_1 = 3$, $l_2 = 2$, then $L = 5, 4, 3, 2$, or $1$ (Fig. 6–7b). If there are three electrons, then $s_1 = s_2 = s_3 = \frac{1}{2}$, and $S = \frac{3}{2}, \frac{1}{2}$, or $\frac{1}{2}$ (Fig. 6–7c). The latter example illustrates the process used to add three vectors. First, two of them are added; thus for $s_1 = s_2 = \frac{1}{2}$, the resultant $S$ is 1 or 0. The subsequent addition of $s_3 = \frac{1}{2}$ results in $S = \frac{3}{2}, \frac{1}{2}$, or $\frac{1}{2}$. Negative values of the quantum numbers $n, l, s, L, S, J$, like negative vectors, do not exist. It is only the quantum numbers obtained by projections on a reference axis, such as $m_l$ and $m_s$, which can have negative values. Negative values are allowed so that projections of the same magnitude but opposite orientation, $\uparrow$ or $\downarrow$, can be distinguished. If $L = 2$, $S = \frac{1}{2}$, then $J = \frac{5}{2}$ or $\frac{3}{2}$. If $L = 1$, $S = 1$, then $J = 2, 1$, or $0$.

## SPECTROSCOPIC TERMINOLOGY FOR ATOMS

The values of $L = 0, 1, 2, 3, \ldots$ are designated by the terms S, P, D, F, $\ldots$ by analogy with the single electron case. The symbol S, for $L = 0$, is not to be confused with the spin quantum number, $S$. The multiplicity, $2S + 1$, is designated as a superscript number prior to the letter used to indicate the value of $L$. Finally, the value of $J$ is indicated as a subscript following the letter used to indicate the value of $L$. Examples are: an atom with $S = 1$, $L = 1$, is designated $^3$P (triplet P); and this state has three component terms, $^3P_2$, $^3P_1$, and $^3P_0$. An atom with $S = \frac{3}{2}$, $L = 0$ is designated by the term $^4$S (quartet S). Only one value of $J$ is allowed, so the complete designation, $^4S_{3/2}$, is not really necessary. Complete term designations should always be given by the novice, however.

For the particular case of two nonequivalent electrons with $l_1 = l_2 = 1$ and $s_1 = s_2 = \frac{1}{2}$, the allowed values of $L$ are then 2, 1, and 0 and the allowed values of $S$ are 1 and 0. Therefore, according to the rules for quantum vector addition, $^3$D-, $^3$P-, $^3$S-, $^1$D-, $^1$P-, and $^1$S-states are allowed. However, if the two electrons are in equivalent p-orbitals, then the Pauli principle excludes the possibility that both electrons can have the same values of both quantum numbers $m_l$ and $m_s$; this results in several of the above terms being ex-

---

* Again, this follows as a result of the uncertainty principle. However, the component vectors can be antiparallel. For example, when $l_1 = l_2 = 1$, then $\mathbf{l}_1 = \mathbf{l}_2 = \sqrt{2}\,\hbar$, and one of the resultant values of $L$ equals zero. The vector $\mathbf{L}$ is then undefined.

cluded. There is no obvious way of deducing which terms are not allowed from quantum vector addition.

## EQUIVALENT ELECTRONS

In order to treat the problem of equivalent electrons, it is convenient to introduce three new quantum numbers, $M_L$, $M_S$, and $M_J$. We have considered the projection of l- and s-vectors for a single electron on the axis in the direction of an imposed magnetic field. If the coupling of the l- and s-vectors is weak enough, they can be considered to behave independently, as a first approximation (Fig. 6–2). Similar considerations can be applied to the L-, S-, and J-vectors for the multielectron atom in magnetic fields of appropriate strength. Just as allowed values of $m_l$ and $m_s$ are obtained from the projections of l and s, so allowed values of $M_L$, $M_S$, and $M_J$ are obtained from projections of L, S, and J. There are $2X + 1$ allowed values for $M_X$, where $X = L$, $S$, or $J$ (Fig. 6–8). Thus there are $2S + 1$ allowed values of $M_S$, and we have an alternative method for arriving at the correct multiplicity of a state. We must regard this discussion as adequate for determining the correct values of $M_S$, $M_L$, and $M_J$ only.*

There is a simple although rather lengthy procedure to follow for equivalent electrons, that is, electrons with the same values of $n$ and $l$. First, list in separate columns all of the allowed values of $m_l$. If $l = 1$, there would be three columns, corresponding to $m_l = 1, 0$, and $-1$. Then list all possible permutations of electrons, taking into account the fact that each electron may be indicated as ↑ or ↓, corresponding to $m_s = +\frac{1}{2}$ or $-\frac{1}{2}$. Two electrons may occupy the same orbital, that is, have the same value of $m_l$, provided that they have opposite spins. Electrons in the same orbital are regarded as indistinguishable, so ↑↓ and ↓↑ represent a single permutation. However, single electrons in each of two different orbitals are regarded as distinguishable, and since there is no spin limitation from the Pauli principle, there are four permutations, ↑↑, ↑↓, ↓↑, and ↓↓. The total number of permutations is

---

* For a single electron, we approximated the splitting of energy levels by an external magnetic field by Eq. (6–16), which states that $\epsilon = B_M m_l H$. However, it is always the total angular momentum and its projections along one axis which are clearly defined, and if a strong enough external magnetic field is present, only the projections remain sharply defined. For a multielectron atom, the total angular momentum is $J$, and in the presence of an external magnetic field, there are $2J + 1$ possible orientations of J, and $2J + 1$ resultant values of $M_J$. An additional factor, $g$, called the Landé interval constant, is required for a precise expression for term splitting, $\epsilon = gB_M M_J H$. If $S = 0$, then $J = L$, the allowed values of $M_J$ and $M_L$ are the same, and $g = 1$. If $S = 0$ for both configurations involved in an atomic spectrum, then the effect of an external magnetic field on an observed spectrum is called the normal Zeeman effect. However, if $S \neq 0$, then $g \neq 1$, and an anomalous Zeeman effect occurs. See discussions of the Landé interval rule, which determines the observed values of $g$.

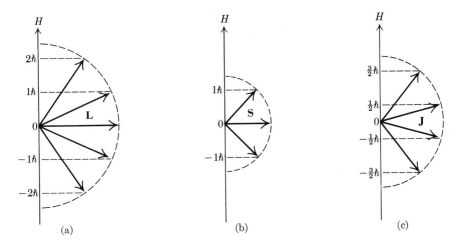

**Fig. 6–8.**  Examples of projections of **L**, **S**, and **J** on the axis representing the direction of a magnetic field, $H$. For (a) and (b), interaction of **L** and **S** is neglected. Correct values of $M_L$ and $M_S$ are obtained, which are important in our discussion of equivalent electrons.  (a) $L = 2$, and therefore **L** has a magnitude of $\hbar\sqrt{6}$. The projections have magnitudes of 2, 1, 0, −1, and −2, in units of $\hbar$, and these numbers are the allowed values of $M_L$.  (b) $S = 1$, and therefore **S** has a magnitude of $\hbar\sqrt{2}$. The projections have magnitudes of 1, 0, and −1 in units of $\hbar$, and these numbers are the allowed values of $M_S$.  (c) $J = \frac{3}{2}$, and therefore **J** has a magnitude of $\hbar\sqrt{\frac{15}{4}}$. The projections have magnitudes of $\frac{3}{2}$, $\frac{1}{2}$, $-\frac{1}{2}$, and $-\frac{3}{2}$ in units of $\hbar$, and these numbers are the allowed values of $M_J$.

illustrated in Table 6–1 for two electrons with $l = 1$, and in Table 6–2 for three electrons with $l = 1$. In the former case, there are a total of 15 permutations and in the latter, 20.

The next step in the procedure is to determine the values of $M_L$ and $M_S$ for each permutation by simple arithmetic addition, since $M_L = \sum m_l$ and $M_S = \sum m_s$. Next, we choose the largest allowed value of $M_L$ and the corresponding largest value of $M_S$. In the case of two equivalent p-electrons (Table 6–1), the largest value of $M_L$ is 2, with $M_S = 0$. It therefore follows that corresponding to these two quantum numbers, $L = 2$, $S = 0$, and $J = 2$, and the correct spectroscopic term designation is $^1D_2$. There are a total of five allowed values of $M_L$ for $L = 2$ obtained as projections of $L$ on a single axis, and there is only one allowed value of $M_S$ corresponding to $S = 0$. Therefore five permutations, corresponding to $M_L = 2, 1, 0, -1$, and −2, with $M_S = 0$ in each case, are associated with the term $^1D_2$.

There are now $15 - 5 = 10$ permutations left for our two equivalent p-electrons. The largest remaining value of $M_L$ equals unity, and the largest $M_S$ equals unity. These correspond to $L = 1$, $S = 1$, with allowed values of $J = 2, 1, 0$; thus there are three spectroscopic terms, $^3P_2$, $^3P_1$, $^3P_0$. For $L = 1$ there are a total of three allowed values of $M_L$: 1, 0, and −1; and

**Table 6–1**

DETERMINATION OF ALLOWED SPECTROSCOPIC TERMS FOR
TWO EQUIVALENT p-ELECTRONS

| 1 | $m_l$ 0 | −1 | $M_L$ | $M_S$ | $L$ | $S$ | $J$ | Spectroscopic term |
|---|---|---|---|---|---|---|---|---|
| ↑↓ | | | 2 | 0 | 2 | 0 | 2 | $^1D_2$ |
| ↑ | ↓ | | 1 | 0 | | | | |
| ↑ | | ↓ | 0 | 0 | | | | |
| | ↑ | ↓ | −1 | 0 | | | | |
| | | ↑↓ | −2 | 0 | | | | |
| ↑ | ↑ | | 1 | 1 | 1 | 1 | 2 | $^3P_2$ |
| ↑ | | ↑ | 0 | 1 | | | | |
| | ↑ | ↑ | −1 | 1 | | | | |
| ↓ | ↑ | | 1 | 0 | | | | $^3P_1$ |
| ↓ | | ↑ | 0 | 0 | | | | |
| | ↓ | ↑ | −1 | 0 | | | | |
| ↓ | ↓ | | 1 | −1 | | | | $^3P_0$ |
| ↓ | | ↓ | 0 | −1 | | | | |
| | ↓ | ↓ | −1 | −1 | | | | |
| | ↑↓ | | 0 | 0 | 0 | 0 | 0 | $^1S_0$ |

for $S = 1$, $M_S = 1$, 0, and −1. Three values each for $M_L$ and $M_S$ correspond to a total of nine permutations, and three of these are associated with each of the terms $^3P_2$, $^3P_1$, and $^3P_0$. There is only one permutation left, and it corresponds to a $^1S_0$ term. Tables 6–1 and 6–2 have the permutations grouped so that the correct values of $M_L$ and $M_S$ are associated with each spectroscopic term.

No attempt has been made to identify properly different configurations with the same values of $M_L$ and $M_S$, since it is not necessary for our purposes. The procedure outlined above always leads to the correct prediction of the number of spectroscopic terms for equivalent electrons, and so can be regarded as basically correct. However, when we state that, for example, two electrons in two separate orbitals with configurations ↑↓ and ↓↑ represent two distinct permutations, we are in effect saying that we know the value of $m_l$ and $m_s$ for each electron. However, the electrons are indistinguishable particles, and so linear combinations of different configurations are required for a proper wave function.

From the application of Hund's rules, we can deduce the relative order of energies of a multiplet structure. Thus for the $^2D$, $^2P$, and $^4S$ terms associated

## Table 6–2

## DETERMINATION OF ALLOWED SPECTROSCOPIC TERMS
## FOR THREE EQUIVALENT p-ELECTRONS

| 1 | $m_l$ 0 | −1 | $M_L$ | $M_S$ | $L$ | $S$ | $J$ | Spectroscopic term |
|---|---|---|---|---|---|---|---|---|
| ↑↓ | ↑ |  | 2 | $\frac{1}{2}$ | 2 | $\frac{1}{2}$ | $\frac{5}{2}$ | $^2D_{5/2}$ |
| ↑ | ↑↓ |  | 1 | $\frac{1}{2}$ |  |  |  |  |
| ↑ | ↑ | ↓ | 0 | $\frac{1}{2}$ |  |  |  |  |
|  | ↑↓ | ↑ | −1 | $\frac{1}{2}$ |  |  |  |  |
| ↑ |  | ↑↓ | −2 | $\frac{1}{2}$ |  |  |  |  |
| ↑↓ | ↑ |  | 2 | $-\frac{1}{2}$ |  |  |  | $^2D_{3/2}$ |
| ↑ | ↑↓ |  | 1 | $-\frac{1}{2}$ |  |  |  |  |
| ↑ | ↑ | ↓ | 0 | $-\frac{1}{2}$ |  |  |  |  |
|  | ↑↓ | ↑ | −1 | $-\frac{1}{2}$ |  |  |  |  |
| ↑ |  | ↑↓ | −2 | $-\frac{1}{2}$ |  |  |  |  |
| ↑↓ |  | ↑ | 1 | $\frac{1}{2}$ | 1 | $\frac{1}{2}$ | $\frac{3}{2}$ | $^2P_{3/2}$ |
| ↓ | ↑ | ↑ | 0 | $\frac{1}{2}$ |  |  |  |  |
| ↑ |  | ↑↓ | −1 | $\frac{1}{2}$ |  |  |  |  |
| ↑↓ |  | ↓ | 1 | $-\frac{1}{2}$ |  |  |  | $^2P_{1/2}$ |
| ↓ | ↓ | ↑ | 0 | $-\frac{1}{2}$ |  |  |  |  |
| ↓ |  | ↑↓ | −1 | $-\frac{1}{2}$ |  |  |  |  |
| ↑ | ↑ | ↑ | 0 | $\frac{3}{2}$ | 0 | $\frac{3}{2}$ | $\frac{3}{2}$ | $^4S_{3/2}$ |
| ↑ | ↑ | ↓ | 0 | $\frac{1}{2}$ |  |  |  |  |
| ↑ | ↓ | ↓ | 0 | $-\frac{1}{2}$ |  |  |  |  |
| ↓ | ↓ | ↓ | 0 | $-\frac{3}{2}$ |  |  |  |  |

with a $p^3$-configuration, we know from Hund's multiplicity rule that the $^4S$-state is the ground state. The $^2D$-state must be of lower energy than the $^2P$-state, from Hund's angular momentum rule.

Finally, there is another rule known as Hund's *fine structure rule* which gives the relative energies of terms with the same value of $S$ and $L$ but with different values of $J$. This rule states that if the subshell is less than half-filled, then the order of energies is *regular*, which means that the term with the largest value of $J$ has the highest energy. If the subshell is more than half-filled, then the order of energies is *inverted*, so that the term with the largest value of $J$ has the lowest energy. This rule follows from the symmetry of "holes" and electrons. Unfortunately, a $p^3$-configuration corresponds to a subshell which is exactly half-filled, so that the fine structure rule does not help us determine the relative energies of, for example, $^2D_{5/2}$ and $^2D_{3/2}$ terms which are associated with a $p^3$-configuration.

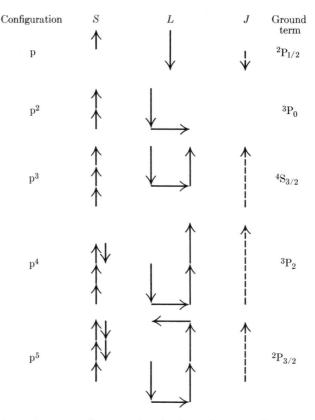

**Fig. 6-9.** Schematic vector diagram, showing how the ground spectroscopic terms for partially filled p-orbitals may be obtained. For the $p^6$-configuration, six **L** vectors enclose a rectangle. From A. C. Candler, *Atomic Spectra.* (London: Cambridge University Press, 1937). (A second edition has been published by Hilger and Watts, Ltd., 1964.)

A method of deducing the ground-state spectroscopic designation for partially filled p- and d-orbitals is shown in Figs 6–9 and 6–10, respectively. The vector additions are uniquely represented *schematically* by a simple method in which only the components of vectors in $\pm z$ directions are added. The resultant of **L** + **S** gives the value of **J**, as we discovered in previous methods.

Finally, it should be pointed out that although we have discussed the elucidation of spectroscopic terms from atomic orbital theory, the reverse sequence was historically important. The development of atomic orbital theory from the spectroscopic evidence represents one of the great triumphs of 20th century science. Spectroscopy has been a great proving ground for the theories of both quantum mechanics and chemistry.

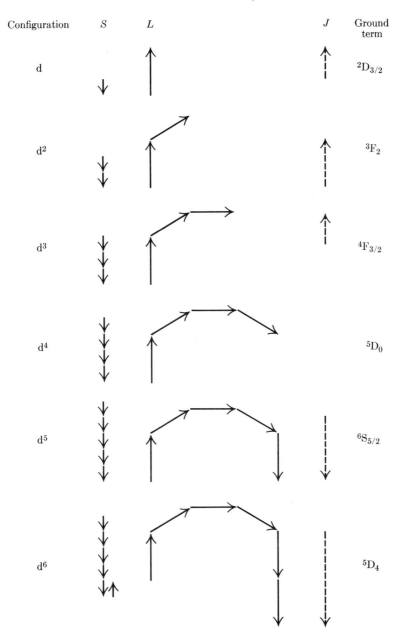

| Configuration | $S$ | $L$ | | $J$ | Ground term |

**Fig. 6–10.** Schematic vector diagram showing how the ground spectroscopic terms for partially filled d-orbitals may be obtained. For the $d^{10}$-configuration ten **L** vectors enclose an octagon. From A. C. Candler, *Atomic Spectra* (London: Cambridge University Press, 1937). (A second edition has been published by Hilger and Watts, Ltd., 1964.)

**PROBLEMS**

1. Discuss the differences between the quantum numbers $l$ and $m_l$, $s$ and $m_s$. What quantum numbers are considered when applying the Pauli principle to the building-up of atoms?

2. Indicate the ground-state electron configurations for atomic H, He, Li, Be, B, C, N, O, F, and Ne, and the corresponding spectroscopic designations.

3. Indicate the ground-state electron configurations and corresponding spectroscopic designations for Al, Si, K, V, Fe, Co, Ni.

4. Given that two electrons have available two equivalent (degenerate) orbitals, show the possible orientations they may have for the state of lower energy.

5. a) In Problem 3, what is the multiplicity of the resultant ground state?
   b) Why do the two electrons not occupy a single orbital?

6. If five electrons have available five equivalent orbitals, show the possible orientations they may have for the ground-state configuration. What is the multiplicity of the ground state?

7. Derive the atomic spectroscopic terms possible for two nonequivalent p-electrons (electrons where $l_1 = l_2 = 1$, $n_1 \neq n_2$).

8. For two equivalent p-electrons in an atom (where $n_1 = n_2$), what spectroscopic terms are possible? Present arguments to show why $^3D$, $^1P$, and $^3S$ terms are not allowed. Arrange the three possible states in order of increasing energy.

9. Of the three terms for two equivalent p-electrons, which ones have fine structure components? Designate the components and arrange them in order of increasing energy.

10. Derive the spectroscopic terms for the following configurations for pairs of nonequivalent electrons: ss, sp, sd, pp, pd, dd.

11. Derive the spectroscopic terms for the following configurations of equivalent electrons: $s^2$, $p^6$, $d^{10}$, p and $p^5$, $p^2$ and $p^4$, d and $d^9$, $d^2$ and $d^8$, $d^3$ and $d^7$, $d^4$ and $d^6$. Indicate fine structure components, where relevant, and their order of energies.

12. The sodium D-line corresponds to a transition $^3P \rightarrow {}^3S$. Write spectroscopic terms, construct an energy level diagram showing fine structure components, and show the transitions which occur.

13. Write an essay on the relative importance of electrostatic and magnetic forces, the Pauli principle, and electronic exchange (resonance), in determining the structure and energy of atoms.

## CHAPTER 7

# MOLECULAR ORBITALS

Molecular orbital and spectroscopic designations exist for molecules which correspond to the description of atoms given in Chapter 6. For certain properties, the terminology for molecules is completely analogous to that for atoms. For other properties differences exist, largely because there is a reduction from spherical symmetry to an axis of symmetry in going from an atom to a diatomic molecule. In some respects the axis of symmetry actually results in a simplification of treatment. We shall discuss spectroscopic terminology for molecules first.

## SPECTROSCOPIC DESIGNATIONS FOR MOLECULES; THE UNITED-ATOM MODEL

Consider an atom which is split into two smaller atoms, which, in turn, are pulled apart to form a molecule. This is called the united-atom model for a molecule. A strong electrostatic field is formed between the two newly formed atoms in the direction of the internuclear axis. This electric field interacts with the electrons in their orbits, with the internuclear axis providing a fixed reference coordinate. From the projections of the vector $\mathbf{L}$, corresponding to the original quantum number $L$, on the internuclear axis, the corresponding molecular quantum number, $M_L$, is obtained. However, for molecules, positive and negative values of $M_L$ of the same absolute magnitude represent degenerate states; that is, they have identical energy.* The only difference between the degenerate molecular states is that the direction of electron rotation is reversed. The absolute value of $M_L$ is designated by $\Lambda$, and since the maximum value of $M_L$ is equal to $L$, $\Lambda$ is given by

$$\Lambda = 0, 1, 2, \ldots, L, \tag{7-1}$$

where $\Lambda$ is the quantum number. The vector projection is defined as $\mathbf{\Lambda}$, which has a magnitude of $\Lambda \hbar$. The value of $\mathbf{\Lambda}$ is an indication of the net velocity of motion of the electron cloud about the internuclear axis. It also correlates with the symmetry of the electron cloud. Thus, when $\Lambda = 0$, the electron cloud has cylindrical symmetry about the internuclear axis, just

---

* This does not apply to states with $M_L = 0$. It is rigorous for larger values of $M_L$, provided that the molecule as a whole is not rotating.

as when $L = 0$, the electron cloud of an atom has spherical symmetry. Just as atomic states of different $L$ are of widely different energies, so molecular states corresponding to different values of $\Lambda$ often have widely different energies. When $\Lambda = 0$, 1, or 2, the corresponding spectroscopic term is designated $\Sigma$, $\Pi$, or $\Delta$, respectively; just as in the atomic case, when $L = 0$, 1, or 2, the spectroscopic term is S, P, or D, respectively.

The united atom has a total spin vector of magnitude $\mathbf{S}$, from which $2S + 1$ projections are obtained when an external magnetic field is applied; hence there are $2S + 1$ values of $M_S$. In the molecule, the total number of electrons is unchanged and the spinning electrons with their associated magnetic moments are unaffected by the electric field. However, there may be a net rotation of the electron cloud about the internuclear axis, in which case a weak magnetic field is formed in the direction of the internuclear axis. There are then $2S + 1$ allowed projections of $\mathbf{S}$ on the internuclear axis. The vector projections are defined in terms of $\mathbf{\Sigma}$ of magnitude $\Sigma\hbar$, where $\Sigma$ is a quantum number for molecules, analogous to $M_S$ for atoms. The allowed values of $\Sigma$ are

$$\Sigma = S, S - 1, \ldots, -S. \tag{7-2}$$

The quantum number $\Sigma$ is not to be confused with the spectroscopic designation used to denote a state with $\Lambda = 0$. The multiplicity of a molecule is $2S + 1$ as it is for an atom. The multiplicity is always designated as a superscript preceding the Greek letter used to indicate the magnitude of $\Lambda$. Molecules always exhibit their full multiplicity in their observed spectra. There are fundamental differences between the behavior of molecules in $\Sigma$-states, as contrasted to $\Pi$- or $\Delta$-states, however. When $\Lambda = 0$ ($\Sigma$-state), there is no net rotation of the electron cloud about the internuclear axis; hence there is no magnetic field along the direction of the internuclear axis, and $\Sigma$ is not defined. However, the multiplicity of a $\Sigma$-state is indicated as a superscript as usual.*

Finally, the sum of the projections $\mathbf{\Lambda}$ and $\mathbf{\Sigma}$ on the internuclear axis is defined as $\mathbf{\Omega}$, of magnitude $\Omega\hbar$:

$$\Omega = \Lambda + \Sigma. \tag{7-3}$$

Equation (7-3) is analogous to $\mathbf{J} = \mathbf{L} + \mathbf{S}$ for atoms. However, in the latter case vector addition is required, whereas for molecules arithmetic addition suffices, since all the quantities in Eq. (7-3) are vector projections along the same internuclear axis. There are $2S + 1$ allowed values of the quantum number $\Omega$ for any given value of $\Lambda \neq 0$. When $\Lambda = 0$ and $\Sigma$ is undefined, then $\Omega$ is also undefined. Therefore no notation is used to indicate a value of $\Omega$. If $\Lambda = 0$ and $S = 0$, then the spectroscopic designation is $^1\Sigma$; if $\Lambda = 0$ and $S = 1$, a $^3\Sigma$-state results. If we are dealing with a molecule

---

* For further details, see the discussion of Hund's case (b) in Chapter 8.

where $\Lambda = 1$ or 2 ($\Pi$- or $\Delta$-state), then $\Sigma$ is defined, and the value of $\Omega$ is indicated by a subscript following the Greek letter designation for the value of $\Lambda$. For example, if $\Lambda = 1$ and $S = 1$, then $\Sigma$ has values 1, 0, and $-1$ in units of $\hbar$. Therefore $\Omega = 2$, 1, or 0, and there are three resultant states, designated as $^3\Pi_2$, $^3\Pi_1$ and $^3\Pi_0$. Since different values of $J$ represent only small energy differences for a given value of $L$ for light atoms, different values of $\Omega$ represent only small energy differences for a given $\Lambda$ for light molecules.

Although we have discussed the spectroscopic notation for diatomic molecules in terms of a united-atom model, the notation, which defines the molecular quantum numbers $S$, $\Lambda$, and $\Omega$, is of universal applicability, regardless of any specific model for molecule formation. We shall discuss two other useful models.

## SEPARATED-ATOM MODEL

Consider two atoms, with quantum numbers $L_1$, $S_1$ for atom number one and $L_2$, $S_2$ for atom number two. As the two atoms combine to form a molecule, the strong electric field in the direction of the internuclear axis is also formed. There are $2L_1 + 1$ resultant values of $M_{L_1}$ and $2L_2 + 1$ resultant values of $M_{L_2}$. The values of $M_L$ for the molecule are given by all possible combinations of

$$M_L = M_{L_1} + M_{L_2}. \tag{7-4}$$

Thus if $L_1 = L_2 = 1$, then the allowed values of $M_{L_1}$ are 1, 0, and $-1$, and those of $M_{L_2}$ are 1, 0, and $-1$. This leads to nine values of $M_L$: 2, 1, 0; 1, 0, $-1$; and 0, $-1$, $-2$. The values 2, $-2$ correspond to a doubly degenerate $\Delta$-state; and two pairs of values, 1, $-1$, correspond to two doubly degenerate $\Pi$-states. Each of the three values of $M_L = 0$ correspond to three different $\Sigma$-states.

The spins of the electrons remain unaffected by the electric field in the molecule, but the manner in which the electrons from the two atoms interact must be taken into account. The allowed combinations of $S_1$ and $S_2$ from the two different atoms are given in terms of the quantum numbers

$$S = (S_1 + S_2), (S_1 + S_2 - 1), \ldots, (S_1 - S_2), \tag{7-5}$$

if $S_1 \geq S_2$. This is analogous to Eq. (6–19) in which total spin for a two-electron system is given. If $S_1 = S_2 = \frac{1}{2}$, then $S = 1$, 0, and both triplet and singlet states are possible for each electronic state derived on the basis of $M_L$ values. Therefore, for the example cited above, a grand total of 12 electronic states for the resultant molecules are possible: $^1\Delta$, $^3\Delta$, $^1\Pi(2)$, $^3\Pi(2)$, $^1\Sigma(3)$, and $^3\Sigma(3)$. Which of these states is the ground electronic state and what is the order of energies of the remaining states? These are questions which we are in no position to answer for such a large number of states, and the use of a separated-atom model for predicting molecular behavior would appear to present serious difficulties.

However, an approach has been developed which can be used to explain otherwise quite mysterious properties of molecules. This approach is called the molecular orbital theory. A prime contribution to its development was made by R. S. Mulliken, for which he was awarded the 1966 Nobel prize in chemistry. It is no accident that he has also had a long and fruitful association with molecular spectroscopy.

We shall discuss the molecular orbital theory and its relation to atomic orbitals, in both united and separated atoms.

## MOLECULAR ORBITALS

The molecular orbital (m.o.) description of molecules represents a logical extension of the description of atomic orbitals. Thus for the hydrogen molecule, the ground electronic state in one particular type of molecular-orbital terminology is designated $(\sigma 1s)^2$. The 1s has the same meaning as in the description of an atomic orbital: 1 is the principal quantum number and s refers to a spherically symmetric atomic orbital. Addition of two 1s atomic orbitals leads to the formation of the $\sigma 1s$ molecular orbital. Since the molecular-orbital formation is readily envisaged in terms of two approaching hydrogen atoms, it is appropriate that the form of m.o. nomenclature used here is called the separated-atom terminology. The designation $\sigma$ is reserved for a resultant molecular orbital which is symmetric about the internuclear axis, and the superscript 2 indicates that two electrons occupy the m.o. The molecular orbital of next highest energy also correlates with 1s atomic orbitals. Furthermore, it is symmetric about the internuclear axis and so is designated by $\sigma$. However, the electron cloud density approaches zero between the two nuclei, so nuclear repulsions are the predominant force along the molecular axis (see Fig. 7–1). The orbital is precisely described as an *antibonding* orbital; that is, it is against bonding. An asterisk is used to indicate that the orbital is antibonding, although this notation is not universal. Two electrons in an antibonding orbital more than cancel the effect of two electrons in a bonding orbital.* Therefore He$_2$, which has the electron configuration $(\sigma 1s)^2(\sigma^*1s)^2$, is an unstable molecule. However, He$_2^+$, with the configuration $(\sigma 1s)^2(\sigma^*1s)^1$ is a stable molecule-ion, since the number of bonding electrons exceeds the number of antibonding electrons. In a similar fashion we shall proceed to a discussion of the formation of heavier homonuclear diatomic molecules.

When electrons with large principal quantum numbers are involved in bond formation, the inner-shell electrons tend to remain in the same con-

---

* In the so-called Linear Combination of Atomic Orbitals to obtain Molecular Orbitals, LCAO-MO, the atomic wave functions can be added or subtracted. Addition leads to bonding molecular orbitals and subtraction leads to antibonding molecular orbitals.

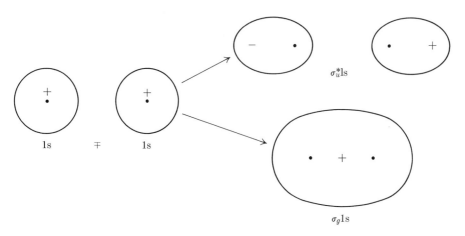

**Fig. 7-1.** The molecular orbitals $\sigma$1s and $\sigma$*1s. These are $\psi$-plots, which result from the subtraction and addition, respectively, of $\psi$'s for two 1s atomic orbitals. The $g$- or $u$-symmetry applies to homonuclear molecules only.

figuration, whether in a separate atom or a molecule. Therefore, for heavier molecules, the $(\sigma 1s)^2(\sigma^*1s)^2$ configuration need not be used, but a simple $KK$-designation suffices to indicate that the lowest shells of each atom are filled.*

The building-up principle used to obtain the electron configuration of atoms of increasing atomic weight also applies to the elucidation of the electron configuration of molecules of increasing molecular weight. The Pauli exclusion principle still applies, though the quantum number $m_l$ is replaced by $\lambda$. The term $\lambda$ signifies the absolute value of the component of the orbital angular momentum of an electron along the internuclear axis, $\lambda = |m_l|$. A single electron which has $\lambda = 0$ occupies a $\sigma$-orbital; when $\lambda = 1$, it occupies a $\pi$-orbital, and when $\lambda = 2$ it occupies a $\delta$-orbital. As we shall see, the quantum numbers $n$ and $l$ for molecules tend to lose the meaning which they had in atoms. The form of the Pauli principle most useful for our purpose is: No two electrons can occupy the same molecular orbital unless they have opposite spins. For a single electron, there is a complete equivalence of (a) $\lambda$ from m.o. terminology and $\Lambda$ of spectroscopic terminology, (b) $\sigma$, $\pi$, $\delta$, from m.o. notation and $\Sigma$, $\Pi$, $\Delta$, respectively, from spectroscopic notation. Furthermore, for two valence electrons with $\lambda_1 \geq \lambda_2$

$$\Lambda = (\lambda_1 + \lambda_2), (\lambda_1 - \lambda_2). \tag{7-6}$$

---

* According to x-ray terminology, filled shells corresponding to the principal quantum number, $n = 1, 2, 3, \ldots$, are designated as $K$-, $L$-, $M$-, $\ldots$ shells, respectively.

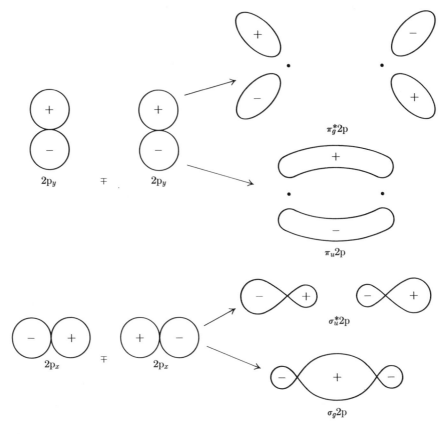

**Fig. 7-2.** Some molecular orbitals formed from 2p atomic orbitals and described in terms of separated-atom nomenclature. Two $2p_z$ atomic orbitals can combine to form molecular orbitals which are degenerate with those obtained from $2p_y$-orbitals. These are $\psi$-plots which are schematic for the m.o.s. The $g$-$u$ symmetry refers to homonuclear diatomic molecules only.

For the electronic ground state of $Li_2$ single electrons from each Li atom are paired in the molecular orbital of next highest energy, $\sigma 2s$, analogous to $\sigma 1s$; so the formation of $Li_2$ from separate atoms can be represented as

$$Li(1s^2 2s^1) + Li(1s^2 2s^1) \rightarrow Li_2(KK)(\sigma 2s)^2.$$

The resultant molecule is stable, since it contains the equivalent of two bonding electrons. The combination of two 2s atomic orbitals can also result in a $\sigma^*$ antibonding orbital, which is analogous to a $\sigma^*$1s-orbital. The formation of $\sigma 2p$, $\sigma^* 2p$, $\pi 2p$, and $\pi^* 2p$ molecular orbitals for homonuclear molecules is represented in Fig. 7-2. Two $2p_z$ atomic orbitals can form either a $\pi^* 2p$ antibonding orbital or a $\pi 2p$ bonding orbital, each of which is degenerate with the corresponding molecular orbital obtained from $2p_y$ atomic orbitals, as shown in Fig. 7–2. The order of increasing energy for these molecular orbitals is shown roughly in Fig. 7–3. Degenerate orbitals are shown side by side. Hund's rules apply to the build-up of molecular orbitals as to atomic orbitals.

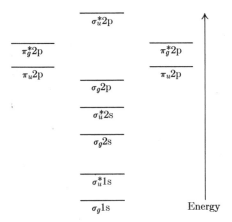

**Fig. 7–3.** Molecular orbital energies (energy scale is arbitrary). Often the $\sigma_g 2p$-orbital is of higher energy than the $\pi_u 2p$-orbitals. The $g$-$u$ symmetry applies to homonuclear diatomic molecules only.

We shall restrict our discussion initially to electronic ground states. As in the discussion of atomic orbitals, attention need only be paid to valence electrons, since only they participate in electronic transitions, and since closed inner shells do not contribute to orbital and spin angular momentum or to bond formation. An even finer distinction can be made for molecular orbitals, as it was also for atomic orbitals, in that filled subshells also do not contribute to orbital or spin angular momentum. For molecular orbitals, any $\sigma$- or $\sigma^*$-orbital can be regarded as a subshell, for when either of these orbitals is filled, the resultant $S$ is zero, and since the electron cloud is symmetric about the internuclear axis, $\Lambda$ is also zero. It is clear that a single valence electron in either of these types of orbitals will result in a doublet state, but since the electron cloud still is axially symmetric, $\Lambda$ is still zero. Any set of degenerate orbitals can also be regarded as a subshell. For example, if the valence electrons of highest energy fill both the $\pi 2p$ orbitals, then $S = 0$, and since the electron cloud is axially symmetric, $\Lambda = 0$, and a $^1\Sigma$-state results. However, if only two electrons are present, according to Hund's rules, they will occupy separate orbitals with parallel spins, so that a triplet state results. The electron cloud will still be axially symmetric and will therefore correspond to a $\Sigma$-state. If only one electron is present in a $\pi p$-orbital, then the electron cloud is not axially symmetric and a $^2\Pi$-state results. If the two electrons are present in the same $\pi p$-orbital, and all lower energy orbitals are filled, then a $^1\Delta$-state results. From Hund's rules, this obviously cannot be the state of lowest energy. The subshells always contain a maximum of two or four electrons.

We have now almost sufficient information to predict both the molecular orbital and spectroscopic designations for ground-state homonuclear diatomic molecules, using the same building-up principles as applied to atomic orbitals. Care has to be exercised, however, when one considers the $\sigma$2p-orbital for the following reasons. Electrons in a bonding orbital stabilize a molecule. Therefore when two atoms approach so that a bonding molecular orbital is formed from the corresponding atomic orbitals, the energy continues to decrease with decreasing internuclear distance until the most stable configuration is reached. For some reason, perhaps related to the geometry of p-orbitals, the energy of $\pi$p-orbitals decreases more rapidly than that of a $\sigma$p-orbital with decreasing internuclear distance. Hence at relatively large internuclear distances, $\pi$p-orbitals are of higher energy than a $\sigma$p-orbital, but at smaller internuclear distances this order is reversed. (See the discussion of united atom-separated atom correlation diagrams below.) It turns out that $B_2$ and $C_2$ have small enough internuclear distances so that the two degenerate $\pi$2p-orbitals have lower energies than the $\sigma$2p-orbital. It follows that $B_2$ has a triplet ground state and $C_2$ has a singlet ground state.* It should be noted that the converse of the above description of the effect of decreasing internuclear distance on the energy of bonding orbitals applies to antibonding orbitals. As might be anticipated, the energy of antibonding orbitals is increased as internuclear distance decreases. Although we have discussed the deduction of spectroscopic designations from molecular orbital descriptions, historically the reverse sequence occurred.

### UNITED-ATOM—SEPARATED-ATOM CORRELATION DIAGRAMS

The above discussion gives us sufficient background to discuss united-atom—separated-atom correlation diagrams, which summarize the information covered so far concerning atomic and molecular orbitals. These diagrams place this information in a different perspective and also yield valuable additional information.

Consider the hypothetical approach of two atoms from infinite distance to such close approach that the two nuclei become fused into a single nucleus. In the range of distances of normal chemical bond formation, let us by some magic means vary continuously the composition of the nuclei with corresponding adjustment in the number of electrons, so that the variable internuclear distance is always that corresponding to the minimum in an electronic potential energy well. For the fusion step we must have at our disposal some means of forcing the nuclei together for the minimum stable internuclear distance and then correcting for this extraneous fusion energy. We are not concerned, therefore, with the passage of two atoms through a potential energy well, as discussed in Chapters 4 and 5. Rather, our primary interest is the

---

* E. A. Ballik and D. A. Ramsay, *J. Chem. Phys.* **31,** 1128 (1959).

energy relationship of individual molecular orbitals which change continuously as a function of internuclear distance, as shown in Fig. 7–4 for heteronuclear diatomic molecules and in Fig. 7–5 for homonuclear diatomic molecules. These are the united-atom—separated-atom correlation diagrams, which are of the utmost practical importance.* The relation between the united-atom—separated-atom correlation diagrams and molecular orbitals is comparable to that between the periodic table and atomic orbitals.

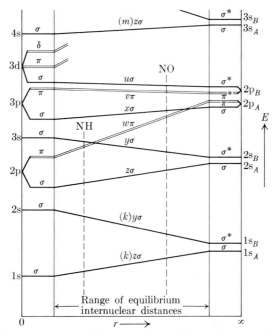

**Fig. 7–4.** United-atom—separated-atom correlation diagram for heteronuclear diatomic molecules. Antibonding orbitals are indicated with asterisks; doubly degenerate orbitals with closely spaced double lines. United-atom terminology can be read from the left-hand side of the diagram, for example, $1s\sigma$, $2s\sigma$; separated-atom terminology from the right, for example, $\sigma^*1s_B$, $\pi 2p_A$. Letter designations for the molecular orbitals are shown in the middle of the diagram, which is not to scale.

Let us discuss the correlation diagram for heteronuclear molecules (Fig. 7–4) first. At infinite separation, two different atoms $A$ and $B$ will have orbitals of different energy because of the difference in nuclear charge. Thus, if atom $A$ has the larger nuclear charge, electrons in its 1s-orbital ($1s_A$) will be of lower energy than in the 1s-orbital ($1s_B$) of atom $B$, and so on. Similarly, when the two atoms are fused into one, the nuclear charge of the united atom is greater than that of the separated atoms, and so the orbital energies are

---

* R. S. Mulliken, *Rev. Modern Physics* **4**, 1 (1932).

correspondingly lower. Thus the pair of electrons in orbital $1s_A$ of the separated atom acquire lower energy in the 1s-orbital of the united atom. However, only two electrons can occupy a 1s-orbital according to the Pauli principle, and so the pair of electrons in the $1s_B$-orbital of the separated atom must occupy the 2s-orbital of the united atom, with an increase in energy. Electrons which acquire more energy as they come under the influence of increased nuclear charge caused by the formation of a molecule from two atoms are, by definition, antibonding, whereas those which drop to lower energy are bonding electrons. Thus the concept of bonding and antibonding orbitals arises in a natural way from the correlation diagram.

There are certain symmetry considerations which must be taken into account. Thus, s-electrons in atoms can only occupy $\sigma$-orbitals in molecules. On the other hand, p-electrons in atoms can occupy either $\sigma$- or $\pi$-orbitals in a molecule, depending upon whether the p-orbitals are oriented along the internuclear axis or are at right angles to it. It is possible for s-electrons in the separated atom to correlate with p-electrons in the united atom by means of a $\sigma$-bond, and this is observed for the $2s_A$-electrons of the separated atom, which have $l = 0$, and the 2p-electrons of the united atom which have $l = 1$. This is therefore a case where $l$ loses its meaning in the molecule. On the other hand, electrons in $\pi$-molecular orbitals can correlate only with electrons in p (or d) atomic orbitals. The closely spaced double lines for $\pi$- or $\delta$-orbitals in Fig. 7–4 indicate that there are two degenerate $\pi$- or $\delta$-orbitals for each molecular orbital designation.

All bonding orbitals are shown with positive slopes; all antibonding orbitals, with negative slopes. The molecular orbital designation for all antibonding orbitals includes an asterisk in their separated-atom designation only. The hydrides, with their small internuclear distances, behave much like united atoms where the concept of antibonding is not meaningful. Letters rather than numbers are often used to designate relative energies of molecular orbitals for the following reasons. Electrons are often promoted from a lower to higher principal quantum number when a separated atom is fused into a united atom. This usually means that they occupy an antibonding orbital, and therefore their energy is increased as the united-atom model is approached (an exception is the $x\sigma$-orbital; see below). Promotion means that the principal quantum number, $n$, loses its meaning for the electron in the molecule. This difficulty is removed by use of the letters $u$, $v$, $w$, $x$, $y$, and $z$. Another way to remove the difficulty is to state clearly whether one is referring to the united atom or the separated atom, it being understood that $n$ may not be meaningful for the molecule. The accepted united-atom terminology is to add the designation of the type of molecular orbital after the designation of principal quantum number and atomic orbital type. Thus $2p\pi$, $3p\sigma$, and $3d\sigma$ are proper united-atom designations for molecular orbitals. In the separated-atom terminology, the molecular orbital type is designated first. The united-atom molecular orbitals listed above are $\pi2p_A$, $\sigma2p_A$, and $\sigma^*2p_B$, respectively, in their separated-atom designations (Fig. 7–4). According to Mulliken's letter designations, the same orbitals are simply $w\pi$, $x\sigma$, and $u\sigma$, respectively. If one is concerned with molecules formed from atoms which have different principal quantum numbers for their valence electrons, then the procedure to follow is to ignore the core electrons in each atom and to feed the valence electrons from the atoms into molecular orbitals, using the usual building-up principle, in the order $z\sigma$, $y\sigma$, $w\pi$ (or $x\sigma$), etc. Accurate predictions of the molecule's electronic properties are often obtained. We shall henceforth emphasize the letter designations here, since they are simpler and more versatile, but the two alternative systems of notation have advantages in particular circumstances.*

Note that the $w\pi$-orbital is of lower energy than the $x\sigma$-orbital for most internuclear distances. Bonding $\pi$-orbitals are generally thought to be of higher energy than bonding $\sigma$-orbitals, and this is true of $w\pi$- and $x\sigma$-orbitals for large internuclear distances. However, from symmetry considerations, the $\pi$ molecular orbitals can only correlate with p (or d) atomic orbitals. Another result of the importance of symmetry is the *noncrossing rule*, which states that orbitals of the same symmetry type cannot cross on the correlation diagram. Note that the $w\pi$-orbital crosses $\sigma$-orbitals, but $\pi$-orbitals cannot cross other $\pi$-orbitals. Both of the above symmetry rules mean that the $w\pi$-orbitals can only correlate with 2p-orbitals in both united and separated atoms. Because of the enhanced nuclear charge on the united atom, the energy of the 2p united-atom orbital is much lower than that of the correlated 2p separated-atom orbital. Furthermore, the overlap of p atomic orbitals to form a $\pi$ molecular orbital becomes much more effective at smaller internuclear distances; hence the large energy drop of the $w\pi$-orbital with decreasing internuclear distance. On the other hand, the $x\sigma$ molecular orbital correlates with a 3p-orbital in the united atom and a $2p_A$-orbital in the separated atom. In this case the effect of increased nuclear charge as internuclear distance decreases is offset by the correlation with an increased principal quantum number, and the $x\sigma$ orbital energy is almost independent of internuclear distance.

Note also that at large internuclear distances, whereas the $w\pi$ bonding orbitals are of higher energy than the $x\sigma$ bonding orbital, the $v\pi$ antibonding orbitals are of lower energy than the $u\sigma$ antibonding orbital. It follows as a corollary that since the bonding character of electrons in a $\pi$-orbital is less than that of electrons in a $\sigma$-orbital, the antibonding character of electrons in a $\pi^*$-orbital is also less than that of electrons in a $\sigma^*$-orbital.

Further discussions of the correlation diagram for heteronuclear molecules perhaps are carried out most conveniently in terms of specific examples. Molecules which come closest to approximating the separated-atom model are

---

* Yet another system of terminology is outlined in C. A. Coulson, *Valence*, 2nd ed. (New York: Oxford University Press), 1963.

those with many electrons, such as NO. By following the vertical line, corresponding to the equilibrium internuclear distance of ground-state NO, we can immediately predict the corresponding electron configuration. We must locate $7 + 8 = 15$ electrons in molecular orbitals, which, according to the Pauli principle, are placed in pairs. The eight molecular orbitals of lowest energy, along the vertical line for NO, range from $(k)z\sigma$ to $v\pi$. All but the latter will contain two electrons, and one will be in the $v\pi$-orbital. Nitric oxide thus has a net of three pairs of bonding electrons and one antibonding electron. The first 14 electrons have a net spin of zero and a net angular momentum about the internuclear axis of zero, so the electron configuration of ground-state NO is determined solely by the single electron in the $v\pi$-orbital. The correct spectroscopic designation is therefore $^2\Pi$.

If an atom has few electrons and takes part in molecule formation, the resultant molecule will approximate the united-atom model. Hydrides come closest to the ideal united-atom case, and we choose NH as an example. For NH, a total of eight electrons are fed into the orbitals $(k)z\sigma$, $(k)y\sigma$, $z\sigma$ and $w\pi$. According to Hund's rule, one electron goes into each of the two degenerate $w\pi$-orbitals, and the electrons have parallel spins. These two electrons result in a net symmetry of the $\pi$-electron cloud about the internuclear axis. The correct spectroscopic designation for ground state NH is therefore $^3\Sigma$.

For the correlation diagram for homonuclear diatomic molecules, an additional symmetry element must be considered. Since the two nuclei are completely equivalent, the electron cloud distributions have point symmetry about the midpoint of the internuclear axis. The corresponding orbitals are either symmetric with respect to inversion about this midpoint, in which case they retain their original sign; or they are antisymmetric, in which case they change sign. Orbitals which are symmetric with respect to inversion are designated $g$, for $gerade$ (even), and those which are antisymmetric are designated by $u$ for $ungerade$ (odd); see Figs. 7–1, 7–2, and 7–3. The additional symmetry present in homonuclear diatomic molecules means that correlations which are allowed for heteronuclear molecules may not be allowed for homonuclear molecules. For example, in the heteronuclear diagram, the $2s\sigma$-orbital correlates with the $\sigma^*1s$-orbital. In the homonuclear correlation diagram, these orbitals become $2s\sigma_g$ and $\sigma_u^*1s$, respectively, and their correlation is not possible because one has $g$-symmetry and the other has $u$-symmetry. Rather, the $2s\sigma_g$- and $\sigma_g2s$-orbitals form the $z\sigma_g$ molecular orbital, and the $2p\sigma_u$- and $\sigma_u^*1s$-orbitals form the $(k)y\sigma_n$ molecular orbital. When applying the noncrossing rule to homonuclear diatomic molecules, the additional $g$-$u$ symmetry must be taken into account. For example, a $\sigma$-orbital can cross another $\sigma$-orbital if one has $g$-symmetry and the other has $u$-symmetry, but a $\sigma_g$-orbital cannot cross another $\sigma_g$-orbital.

The homonuclear molecular-orbital correlation diagram has also been constructed with antibonding orbital energy levels shown with negative slopes, and bonding orbital energies shown with positive slopes. Since we have made no attempt to show quantitative energy relationships among the

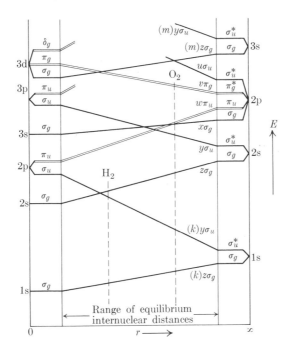

**Fig. 7-5.** United-atom—separated-atom correlation diagram for homonuclear diatomic molecules. The $g$-$u$ symmetry, not present in heteronuclear molecules, causes striking changes in the diagram. The diagram is not drawn to scale.

various orbitals, and since the internuclear distance scale is not specified, we have not used curved lines to connect the united-atom and separated-atom orbitals as in Mulliken's original diagram. The average energy of an electron is markedly dependent on its environment and not solely on the orbital it occupies. It would be impossible to construct diagrams which are accurate for all electronic states of all molecules, and for our purposes, the simple diagrams shown here are adequate.

## PROBLEMS

1. Discuss the quantum numbers important in determining the electron configuration of diatomic molecules, and how they are determined.

2. Atoms with $^3P$-configurations combine to form diatomic molecules. Deduce the spectroscopic designations of all possible combinations of the resultant S and L for the allowed molecular states. (We are not concerned here with $+$, $-$ or $g$, $u$ symmetry.)

3. Repeat Problem 2 for the combination of (a) a $^1$S- and $^1$P-atom (b) a $^1$S- and a $^3$P-atom.

4. Repeat Problem 2 for $^2P + ^3D$ atoms. (If $\Lambda = 3$, a $\Phi$-state results.)

5. A $^3\Delta$-state has components of slightly different energies. What quantum number is used to indicate these components and how are its allowed values deduced? Give the correct designation of the components. Do comparable components exist for a $^3\Sigma$-state? Why?

6. Give the correct designations for the sublevels of (a) a $^2\Pi$-state (b) a $^4\Delta$-state.

7. Write the m.o. and spectroscopic designations for the ground state of $N_2$ and $O_2$. Which has the greater bond-dissociation energy, $N_2$ or $N_2^+$, $O_2$ or $O_2^+$? Why?

8. Determine the ground-state m.o. and spectroscopic designations for $Li_2$, $Be_2$, $B_2$, $C_2$, $F_2$, and $Ne_2$. Arrange all homonuclear diatomic molecules from the second row of the periodic table in a rough order of decreasing bond-dissociation energies.

9. Deduce the ground-state m.o. and spectroscopic designations for $O_2^+$ and $NO^+$.

10. Determine the m.o. and spectroscopic designations of the first excited states of all molecules discussed in the previous problems.

11. Deduce the m.o. and spectroscopic designations of all diatomic hydrides of elements from the second period.

CHAPTER 8

# MOLECULAR MODELS

We shall consider here in some detail the four different models necessary to account for the different observed types of spectra of diatomic molecules. These models are the rigid rotor, the symmetric top, and molecules which conform to the rules of Hund's cases (a) and (b).

## THE RIGID ROTOR

For the rigid rotor model of a diatomic molecule, the moment of inertia about the $A$-axis, which passes through the two nuclei, is considered to be zero. On the other hand, the rotation of the molecule as a whole about the $B$-axis, which passes through the effective center of mass of the molecule and is at right angles to the $A$-axis, is considered responsible for the entire angular momentum of the molecule. The angular momentum of the molecule can indeed be represented as a vector along the $B$-axis (Fig. 8–1), and it is for this reason that the rotational constant is called $B$, or more properly, $B_v$. The subscript $v$ indicates a dependence of the rotational constant on the vibrational quantum number, and hence implies that vibration-rotation interaction is not of negligible importance. Otherwise, the rigid rotor model is satisfactory for $^1\Sigma$-molecules. This means that for a $^1\Sigma$-state, the electron cloud has cylindrical symmetry about the internuclear axis, there is no *net* motion of the electrons about the internuclear axis, and hence the component of angular momentum along the internuclear axis is zero.

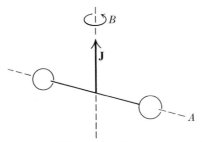

**Fig. 8–1.** Representation of a rigid rotor, which revolves about the $B$-axis. The arrow indicates the total angular momentum vector, **J**.

107

## THE SYMMETRIC TOP

All diatomic molecules which have $\Lambda \neq 0$, that is, molecules which are not in a $\Sigma$-state, are really better models of a symmetric top than of a rigid rotor. The symmetric-top model is particularly precise for $^1\Pi$- and $^1\Delta$-states. For $^1\Pi$- and $^1\Delta$-molecules, the electron cloud does not have complete cylindrical symmetry; there is a *net* rapid motion of the electrons about the internuclear or $A$-axis; hence there is a component of angular momentum along the $A$-axis. The moment of inertia of the electrons is small. However, because of their very rapid motion compared to the speed of molecular rotation, the angular-momentum vector along the $A$-axis is comparable in magnitude to that along the $B$-axis. In fact, three axes must be considered, labeled $A$, $B$, and $C$, which all pass through the effective center of mass and are all at right angles to one another. These are called the principal axes or axes of symmetry. For a rigid rotor, the moments of inertia about the $B$- and $C$-axes are equal, and by convention are designated as $I_B$, whereas $I_A = 0$. For a symmetric top, again $I_B = I_C$, and by accepted convention $I_B$ is specified; $I_A$ is not zero, although it is appreciably less than $I_B$. (Do not confuse moment of inertia, $I$, which is the rotational analog of mass, with angular momentum, which depends on both $I$ and velocity of rotation, $\omega$.) As pointed out by Herzberg, a symmetric-top model of a diatomic model can be represented as a dumb-bell on which there is a light flywheel (see Fig. 8–2a).

We shall now consider in greater detail the angular-momentum components and the total rotational motion of the symmetric-top molecule. As discussed in Chapter 7, the quantum number $\Lambda$ indicates the magnitude of the component of electronic motion about the internuclear axis. The magnitude of the resultant electronic angular-momentum vector along the internuclear axis is indicated by the corresponding vector $\boldsymbol{\Lambda}$, of magnitude $\hbar\Lambda$. The rotation of the two nuclei about the $B$-axis results in an angular-momentum vector, $\mathbf{N}$, along this axis. The total resultant angular momentum of the molecule is represented by $\mathbf{J}$, given as the vector sum of $\mathbf{N}$ and $\boldsymbol{\Lambda}$ (Fig. 8–2b).

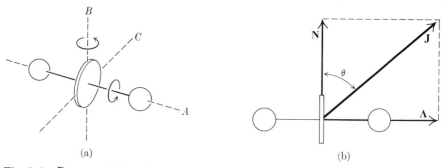

(a)                                                        (b)

**Fig. 8–2.** Representation of a symmetric top, showing (a) the principal axes and (b) the components of angular momentum.

The total angular momentum of the symmetric top is given by $M = \hbar\sqrt{J(J+1)}$ as for a rigid rotor; the difference is that for a symmetric top $\mathbf{J}$ is inclined at an angle $\theta$ to the $B$-axis, where $0 < \theta < 90°$. The resultant molecular rotation is about this $\mathbf{J}$-vector, meaning that the top wobbles, a motion familiar to every child.* If $\Lambda = 0$, that is, if $\Lambda$ is undefined, then $\mathbf{J} = \mathbf{N}$, and we have reverted to the rigid rotor model.

It can be seen from Fig. 8–2(b) that $\mathbf{J} > \Lambda$; therefore $J(J+1) > \Lambda^2$, and, in fact, the smallest allowed value of the quantum number $J$ is $J = \Lambda$. Therefore rotational levels corresponding to $J < \Lambda$ are missing, and this provides a means of identifying symmetric top molecules.

The total energy of rotation is given by

$$E = \tfrac{1}{2}I_A\omega_A^2 + \tfrac{1}{2}I_B\omega_B^2 + \tfrac{1}{2}I_C\omega_C^2$$
$$= \tfrac{1}{2}I_A\omega_A^2 + I_B\omega_B^2$$
$$= \frac{P_A^2}{2I_A} + \frac{P_B^2}{I_B}.$$

However, $P_A = \Lambda\hbar$, and

$$P_B^2 + P_C^2 = 2P_B^2 = N^2\hbar^2 = [J(J+1) - \Lambda^2]\hbar^2.$$

Therefore

$$E = \left[\frac{\Lambda^2}{2I_A} + \frac{J(J+1) - \Lambda^2}{2I_B}\right]\hbar^2 \text{ ergs}$$

which is readily converted into an equation in wave number units

$$F(J) = \left[\frac{J(J+1)}{I_B} + \left(\frac{1}{I_A} - \frac{1}{I_B}\right)\Lambda^2\right]\frac{h}{8\pi^2c} \text{ cm}^{-1}.$$

But from Eq. (2–13),

$$B = \frac{h}{8\pi^2cI_B} \text{ cm}^{-1},$$

and it follows that

$$A = \frac{h}{8\pi^2cI_A} \text{ cm}^{-1}.$$

By substitution for $I_A$ and $I_B$ in terms of $A$ and $B$ into the equation for $F(J)$, it follows that

$$F(J) = BJ(J+1) + (A - B)\Lambda^2 \text{ cm}^{-1}. \tag{8-1}$$

Since $I_A$ is small compared to $I_B$, $A$ is large compared to $B$. It can be seen that the rotational levels of a symmetric top differ from those of a rigid rotor

---

* The wobbling of the molecule is due to an internal force, however.

in that they are shifted by a constant number of reciprocal centimeter units, $(A - B)\Lambda^2$, and, as we have already pointed out, levels corresponding to $J < \Lambda$ are missing.

There are two other important properties of symmetric-top molecules. We have indicated that rotation of the electrons and of the internuclear axis are coupled to form a total resultant molecular rotation. This coupling can occur in the sense shown in Fig. 8–2b, or as a mirror-image of Fig. 8–2b, with the mirror placed along the $B$-axis. Thus $\Lambda$ can be oriented in one direction for a net clockwise electronic rotation about the $A$-axis, or in the opposite direction for net counter-clockwise motion when viewed from the same end of the molecule. In other words, left-handed or right-handed molecules are equally probable. As we shall see, this has a direct bearing on observed spectra of symmetric tops, and it is also of great importance in the spectra of the slightly more complex molecules which conform to Hund's case (a).

**Analysis of spectra involving symmetric tops.** The most striking difference between electronic spectra for symmetric tops, as contrasted to rigid rotors, is that the bands are double-headed, instead of single-headed. Whereas for the rigid rotor the selection rule is $\Delta J = \pm 1$, for a symmetric top the rule is $\Delta J = 0, \pm 1$.* The additional allowed transitions, corresponding to $\Delta J = 0$, result in the appearance of a new branch in each band, called the $Q$-branch, which is responsible for the second band head.

It is a straightforward procedure to derive formulas from Eq. (8–1) for the $P$-, $Q$-, and $R$-branches of the bands observed which involve states where $\Lambda \neq 0$, that is, which involve symmetric tops. For a given electronic state $\Lambda$ is a constant, and often $\Delta\Lambda = 0$ for an electronic transition. We shall treat this case only—the extension to the case where $\Delta\Lambda \neq 0$ is a simple extension of our treatment. Upper-state rotational energy levels are obtained by adding the energy of electronic excitation, $T_e$, and vibrational excitation of the upper-state $G(v')$ to Eq. (8–1):

$$T' = F(J') + T_e + G(v') = B'J'(J' + 1) + (A' - B')\Lambda^2 + T_e + G(v'),$$
$$\text{(8–2)}$$

$$T'' = F(J'') + G(v'') = B''J''(J'' + 1) + (A'' - B'')\Lambda^2 + G(v''). \quad \text{(8–3)}$$

Energies of the lines of any given branch of a band are obtained by subtraction of Eq. (8–3) from Eq. (8–2), after making the appropriate substitution that expresses $J'$ in terms of $J''$. Recall that for the $P$-branch, $J' = J'' - 1$; for the $R$-branch, $J' = J'' + 1$; and for the $Q$-branch, $J' = J''$. The last three terms of the upper-state equation and the last two terms of the lower-state equation above are constants for any given band. The difference between them is $\bar{\nu}_{00}$.

---

* There are now two ways in which angular momentum of the molecule can change, through $N$ and $\Lambda$, and it is possible to envisage both of these changing with no resultant change in $J$.

The resultant equations, of general applicability to a band involving symmetric tops (all with $J = J''$), are

$$R(J) = \bar{\nu}_R = \bar{\nu}_{00} + B'(J+1)(J+2) - B''J(J+1), \qquad (8\text{-}4)$$

$$Q(J) = \bar{\nu}_Q = \bar{\nu}_{00} + B'J(J+1) - B''J(J+1), \qquad (8\text{-}5)$$

$$P(J) = \bar{\nu}_P = \bar{\nu}_{00} + B'J(J-1) - B''J(J+1). \qquad (8\text{-}6)$$

The $P$- and $R$-branch equations are identical with those of a rigid rotor (Chapter 3) except that $\bar{\nu}_{00}$ now includes a term which involves $\Lambda^2$. As for a rigid rotor, the $P$- and $R$-branches can be fitted to a single Fortrat parabola. Recall that

$$F(J+1) = B(J+1)(J+2); \qquad F(J) = BJ(J+1);$$

$$F(J-1) = BJ(J-1);$$

also that $m = -J''$ for the $P$-branch, and $m = J'' + 1$ for the $R$-branch. For the $Q$-branch, $m = J''$.

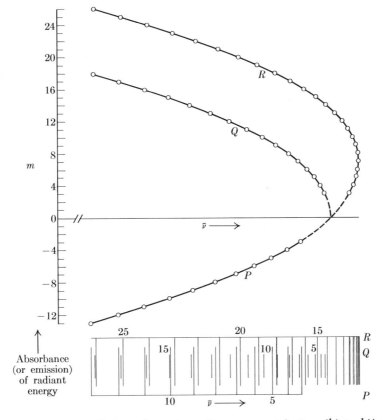

**Fig. 8-3.** Fortrat parabola and spectrum for a symmetric top ($^1\Delta \leftarrow {}^1\Delta$) band. For convenience, $R$- and $P$-branch lines are extended above and below, respectively. Note the missing lines near the origin.

The Fortrat parabola and the corresponding spectrum are shown for a $^1\Delta \leftarrow {}^1\Delta$ electronic band in Fig. 8–3. Note the missing points on the parabola, in addition to the one corresponding to the null gap, and the absence of the corresponding spectral lines. Note also the fashion in which a second band head is formed by the $Q$-branch.

We studied in Chapter 3 the use of combination differences, $\Delta_2 F(J)$, for the analysis of a spectrum involving $P$- and $R$-branches. By use of these combination differences, involving pairs of levels in which a single intervening level is neglected (Fig. 3–4), upper-state rotational levels can be analyzed from an observed spectrum, independent of any interference from lower-state levels, and conversely. The presence of a $Q$-branch makes it possible to analyze successive levels of either upper or lower states, in terms of combination differences $\Delta_1 F(J')$ or $\Delta_1 F(J'')$, obtained as follows:

$$\Delta_1 F(J') = R(J) - Q(J)$$
$$= Q(J+1) - P(J+1), \tag{8–7}$$
$$\Delta_1 F(J'') = R(J) - Q(J+1)$$
$$= Q(J) - P(J+1). \tag{8–8}$$

There are thus two ways of arriving at each set of combination differences; these provide excellent confirmation of a correct analysis. From the above formulas and from the appropriate substitutions of the type $F(J) = B_v J$ $(J+1)$ into Eqs. (8–4) through (8–6) and, subsequently, the substitutions into Eqs. (8–7) and (8–8), it can be deduced that

$$\Delta_1 F(J) = 2B_v(J+1),^* \qquad \text{or} \qquad B_v = \Delta_1 F(J)/2(J+1),$$

for either the upper or lower vibrational state.

The above discussion provides enough information for the analysis of the fine structure of the bands involving either a $^1\Pi$- or $^1\Delta$-state, for small values of $J$ and/or comparatively low resolution. For large values of $J$, and/or for comparatively high resolution, the effect of $\Lambda$-doubling is observed: individual rotational levels are made to split.† We shall postpone discussion of the problem of spectral analysis where $\Lambda$-doubling is important until after a discussion of the symmetry properties of the rotational levels in Chapter 9.

Many examples have been observed of transitions between electronic states which conform to the symmetric-top model. In principle, there is no reason why a vibration-rotation band should not be observed for a symmetric top, and it is convenient to discuss here the form of such a band. If Fig. 8–3 were redrawn for the case where $B'$ is only slightly less than $B''$, where $v' = 1$, $v'' = 0$, and where no change in electronic configuration occurs,

---

\* Here $J$ is the quantum number of the lower of the two rotational levels involved in the combination difference, $\Delta_1 F(J)$.

† The effect of $\Lambda$-doubling is particularly noticeable for hydrides.

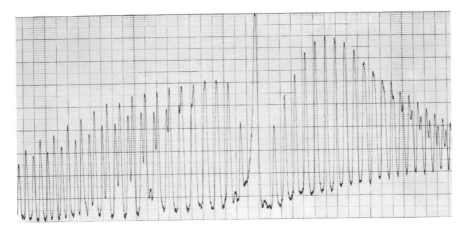

**Fig. 8-4.** The nitric oxide fundamental band in the i.r. region. In this spectrum Λ-doubling is not important. The doubling of lines is due to the superposition of fundamental bands for both the $^2\Pi_{1/2}$- and $^2\Pi_{3/2}$-states. Absorbance is plotted vs. wave number. Plate courtesy of R. Swindlehurst.

we would have the correct diagram corresponding to a vibration-rotation band of a symmetric-top molecule. For this case, the energies of all $Q$-branch lines would be similar and would probably be so close together that they would not be resolved by the infrared spectrometer. Rather, they would appear as a single, intense, slightly asymmetric line where the null gap existed for a rigid-rotor i.r. band. The $P$- and $R$-branches would show the usual slight contraction of spacing as a function of increasing energies of transitions, but they would have lines missing which correspond to the hypothetical transitions to or from missing energy levels, where $J < \Lambda$. In practice, a vibration-rotation band for a symmetric-top diatomic molecule has never been observed. However, the above considerations are very relevant to our discussion of the vibration-rotation spectrum of the slightly more complex, but very interesting, molecule, nitric oxide, NO (Fig. 8-4).

**Interaction of $\Lambda$ and $\Sigma$.** The molecular models we have considered so far have been applicable to molecules which have $S$, the total spin quantum number, equal to zero. The multiplicity is therefore $2 \times 0 + 1 = 1$, and singlet states result. If $\Lambda$ also is equal to zero, we have a $^1\Sigma$-state, which corresponds to the rigid-rotor model. If $\Lambda = 1$ or $2$, we have a $^1\Pi$- or $^1\Delta$-state, respectively, which corresponds to the symmetric-top model. It is now appropriate to consider models which are applicable to multiplet states, that is, states where $S \neq 0$.

As we saw in Chapter 7, when $\Lambda \neq 0$, that is, when $\Lambda$ is defined, it represents a vector component of electron orbital motion along the internuclear axis. This causes a magnetic field to exist along the internuclear axis. When $S \neq 0$ and $\Lambda \neq 0$, there is a component of $\mathbf{S}$ along the internuclear axis which interacts with the magnetic field. The component of $S$ along the internuclear axis is designated by $\Sigma$. Finally, $\Lambda$ and $\Sigma$ can be added arithmetically to give a resultant $\Omega$. There are $2S + 1$ allowed values of $\Omega$ for a given value of $\Lambda$. Thus if $\Lambda = 2$ and $S = 1$, then the allowed values of $\Omega$ are 1, 2, and 3. Three electronic states of slightly different energies result, which are $^3\Delta_1$, $^3\Delta_2$, and $^3\Delta_3$. The energies are equispaced on an energy-level diagram (Fig. 8–5).

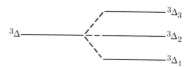

**Fig. 8-5.** The splitting of a $^3\Delta$-state caused by the interaction of $\Sigma$ and $\Lambda$.

The magnitude of the magnetic field between the atoms is proportional to $\Lambda$, and hence is zero when $\Lambda$ is zero, that is, when $\Lambda$ is undefined. The magnitude of the interaction of $\Sigma$ with the magnetic field is proportional to the value of $\Sigma$. For a given $\Sigma$, the splitting of energy levels is given by

$$T_e = T_0 + A\Lambda\Sigma, \tag{8-9}$$

where $T_0$ is the energy level corresponding to no spin interaction. The constant $A$ increases in value with increasing atomic weight. The splitting into multiple electronic states, as a result of the interaction of the electron spin with the magnetic field caused by orbital motion of the electrons, does not affect the degeneracy of the individual rotational levels because $\Lambda$ can have two equivalent orientations for $\Lambda \neq 0$. Thus, if a single electronic state is split into triplet electronic components, the rotational levels of each of these three components remain doubly degenerate as a first approximation (however, see the discussion of the symmetric top).

### HUND'S CASE (a)

A series of rules were devised by Hund to determine the total resultant angular momentum of molecules with multiplicities greater than unity. Each of his sets of rules describes a particular molecular model. For Hund's case (a), the total electronic angular-momentum vector along the internuclear axis, the magnitude of which is designated by $\Omega$ (see the previous section), is coupled with the angular-momentum vector, $N$, resulting from rotation of the internuclear axis, to form a resultant $J$ (Fig. 8–6). Hund's case (a) is therefore identical to the symmetric top model, except

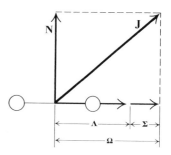

**Fig. 8-6.** Vector diagram for a Hund's case (a) molecule. The rotating molecule wobbles about the $J$-vector.

that $\Lambda$ for the symmetric top is replaced by $\Omega$ for the case (a) model. The observed spectra are therefore similar, with $P$-, $Q$-, and $R$-branches to each band, but the bands are split into multiplet components, the number of which corresponds to the multiplicity of the molecule. Thus, whereas there are three branches to a $^1\Pi$-$^1\Pi$ electronic band, where both electronic states correspond to symmetric tops, there would be a total of nine branches for a $^3\Pi$-$^1\Pi$ transition, if it could occur, where the $^3\Pi$-state corresponds to Hund's case (a). There would be, in fact, three separate bands, one for each of the states, $^3\Pi_2$, $^3\Pi_1$, and $^3\Pi_0$, and each band would be composed of three branches. Energy levels for all the components of a $^3\Pi$-state are represented in Fig. 8-7.

Since Hund's case (a) applies to molecules where $S > 0$, $\Lambda > 0$, typical examples are $^2\Pi$-, $^3\Pi$-, and $^2\Delta$- and $^3\Delta$-states.

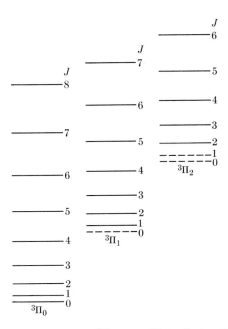

**Fig. 8-7.** Energy-level diagram for a $^3\Pi$-state. Note that rotational levels where $J < \Omega$ are missing. The slight splitting of levels caused by $\Lambda$-doubling has been ignored.

## HUND'S CASE (b)

The model for Hund's case (b) corresponds to multiplet $\Sigma$-states, that is, multiplet states for which $\Lambda = 0$. For this case, since $\Lambda$ is undefined, there is no magnetic field between the atoms with which $S$ can interact. Therefore $\Sigma$ is also undefined. As a result, the spin vector $\mathbf{S}$ couples directly with $\mathbf{N}$, the angular-momentum vector associated with the rotation of the internuclear axis. The result gives **J**, the total angular-momentum vector of the molecule (Fig. 8–8). The molecule as a whole precesses about **J**.

The allowed values of $J$ are given by

$$J = (N + S), (N + S - 1), \ldots, (N - S).$$

Since $J$ cannot be negative, values of $(N - S)$ cannot be less than zero.

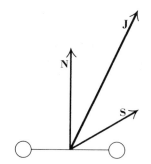

**Fig. 8–8.** Vector diagram for a multiplet Σ-state, which conforms to Hund's case (b). Again the rotating molecule wobbles about the axis through the **J**-vector.

Thus, if $S = \frac{1}{2}$, that is, if we have a $^2\Sigma$-state, then for $N = 0$, $J = \frac{1}{2}$ only; for $N = 1$, $J = \frac{3}{2}$ or $\frac{1}{2}$; for $N = 2$, $J = \frac{5}{2}$ or $\frac{3}{2}$; etc. (Fig. 8–9). In general, rotational levels of a $^2\Sigma$-state are doubled, with the single exception noted. Two equations are required to describe the split rotational levels:

$$F_1(N) = B_v N(N + 1) + \tfrac{1}{2}\gamma N, \tag{8–10}$$

$$F_2(N) = B_v N(N + 1) - \tfrac{1}{2}\gamma(N + 1), \tag{8–11}$$

where $\gamma$ is the splitting constant for the two sublevels corresponding to the two values of $J$ which are associated with each value of $N$. Generally, $\gamma$ is small, which indicates that the coupling between **N** and **S** is weak. In Eqs. (8–10) and (8–11) $F_1(N)$ refers to $J = N + \frac{1}{2}$ and $F_2(N)$ to $J = N - \frac{1}{2}$.

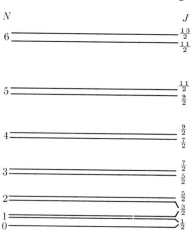

**Fig. 8–9.** Energy levels of a $^2\Sigma$-state. The splitting because of interaction of **N** and **S** is greatly exaggerated.

If $S = 1$, $\Lambda = 0$, we are concerned with a $^3\Sigma$-state. From the above considerations, one might predict that three allowed values of $J$ exist for each value of $N$, except when $(N - S) < 0$, and this is correct. However, in addition to the S-N coupling, the two unpaired electrons interact, so that, in addition to $\gamma$, a second splitting constant, $\lambda$, is required. Fundamental information about the nature of the spin-spin interaction is obtainable from a study of spectra involving $^3\Sigma$-states, but the treatment is beyond the scope of this work.

**PROBLEMS**

1. Classify molecules which have the following spectroscopic designations as typical examples of rigid rotors, symmetric tops, or molecules which conform to Hund's cases (a) or (b): $^2\Pi$, $^1\Sigma$, $^3\Sigma$, $^3\Delta_2$, $^3\Delta_1$, $^3\Delta_0$, $^3\Pi$, $^1\Delta$, $^2\Sigma$.

2. Draw molecular-orbital pictures for all of the homonuclear diatomic molecules obtained from the second period of the periodic table. Classify the molecules as typical rigid rotors, symmetric tops, etc.

3. Repeat Problem 2 for the molecules NO, CH, AlH, CO, and BO.

4. A molecule is found to give an i.r. spectrum in which the first lines of both the $P$- and $R$-branches are missing, and a large asymmetric line occurs in the center of the band. What is the electronic configuration of the molecule? Why?

5. The following data are part of the fundamental band obtained as the first example of a vibration-rotation band for a symmetric-top molecule. The rotational levels are apparently doubly degenerate; that is, no $\Lambda$-doubling can be detected. Label all spectral lines. Determine $B_0$ and $B_1$. Classify the electronic state of the molecule and explain the basis for your classification. What can be said about the two nuclei? Do you think it likely that a molecule would have such an electronic configuration in its ground state? Why?

$$\bar{\nu},\ cm^{-1}\ in\ vacuo$$

| | |
|---|---|
| 1209.52 | |
| 1211.07 | |
| 1212.61 | |
| 1214.15 | |
| 1215.68 | |
| 1220.0 — 1220.2 | large, asymmetric line |
| 1224.67 | |
| 1226.15 | |
| 1227.61 | |
| 1229.07 | |
| 1230.52 | |

6. Compute the wave numbers of the missing line in Problem 5.

7. The following wave numbers in vacuo are obtained for a single band in the electronic spectrum of the diatomic hydride:

| | |
|---|---|
| 30,005.03 | 30,143.08 |
| 24.27 | 146.44 |
| 43.47 | 148.97 |
| 61.43 | 150.65 |
| 78.55 | 174.78 |
| 94.82 | 185.16 |
| 110.25 | 194.70 |
| 113.61 | 203.40 |
| 121.18 | 211.25 |
| 124.84 | 218.26 |
| 127.92 | 224.43 |
| 133.81 | 229.76 |
| 138.87 | |

Assign all lines and determine $B'$ and $B''$ on the basis of $\Delta_1 F(J)$s. Report $\Delta_1 F(8')$ and $\Delta_1 F(4'')$, each on the basis of lines from two pairs of branches. What electronic states are involved in the transition? Why? Assume that $\Lambda$-doubling is not important here.

## CHAPTER 9

# SYMMETRY AND SELECTION RULES

A general rule in spectroscopy is that the greater the degree of symmetry in a molecule, the simpler will be its observed spectrum. In other words, the larger the number of elements of symmetry, the fewer the number of allowed transitions. It is our purpose here to discuss in some detail the symmetry elements important for diatomic molecules and their relation to the selection rules for spectroscopic transitions.

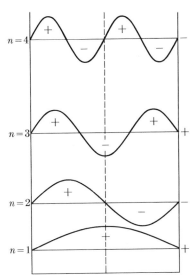

**Fig. 9-1.** Energy levels and wave functions for a particle in a box.

The energy levels and corresponding wave functions, $\psi$, for the quantum mechanical particle-in-the-box are shown in Fig. 9-1. It can be seen that there is a vertical plane of symmetry at the midpoint of the box, and that all $\psi$-functions either are totally symmetric with respect to reflection in this plane, or else they change sign only, in which case they are called antisymmetric functions. If their sign remains unchanged, they are designated plus (+) states, but if their sign changes, they are designated with a minus (−) sign. The simple particle-in-the-box problem is very relevant to behavior of electronic wave functions. As we shall discuss in more detail later, molecular electronic wave functions exhibit the same symmetric or antisymmetric behavior with respect to reflection through a plane which passes through both nuclei. If $\psi_{elec}$ retains its sign, it is a $(+)$-state, but if it changes sign, it is a $(-)$-state. If the wave functions correspond to a $\Sigma$-state, the corresponding molecular states are designated $\Sigma^+$ or $\Sigma^-$, respectively, and opposite selection rules apply to transitions involving these two states. The $(+, -)$-symmetry also applies to $\Pi$- and $\Delta$-states, but is not designated as such, for reasons discussed later.

Another type of symmetry of importance is that with respect to *inversion*. This amounts to replacing the $x_i$-, $y_i$-, and $z_i$-coordinates for each particle by $-x_i$, $-y_i$, and $-z_i$. The corresponding operation on a $\psi$-function means that the coordinates $x_i$, $y_i$, $z_i$ of each point contained within the function are changed to $-x_i$, $-y_i$, $-z_i$. As an example, consider the $\psi$-functions for s-, p- and d-orbitals (Fig. 6-1). A $\psi$-function which remains unchanged upon inversion is defined as $(g)$, for *gerade* or even, and a $\psi$-function which changes sign upon inversion is defined as $(u)$, for *ungerade* or odd. The symbols $(g)$ and $(u)$ are analogous to $(+)$ and $(-)$, respectively, but different symbols are used to indicate that a different symmetry operation is involved. According to the above definition, the function for the s-orbital is a $(g)$ function; $\psi$ for a p-orbital is $u$, and $\psi$ for a d-orbital is $(g)$. It turns out that $\psi$ for an f-orbital is $(u)$, and in general, when the quantum number $l$ is even, $(g)$ states result, and when $l$ is odd, $(u)$ states result. The $(g)$-$(u)$ symmetry is commonly incorporated into the notation used for homonuclear diatomic molecular wave functions (Figs. 7-1, 7-2 and 7-3). However, we shall use it in Chapter 9 consistently to describe symmetry with respect to inversion, regardless of the particular wave function involved.*

The particle-in-the-box wave functions correspond to a particle which has *translational* motion. There are corresponding $\psi$-functions for *vibrational* and *rotational motion of molecules*, as well as for *electronic* motion. The vibrational $\psi$-functions are governed solely by the internuclear distance for a given molecule. They are always symmetric and so are of no further concern to us here. The rotational wave functions for a rigid rotor are identical in form to the angular part of $\psi$ for electronic states of the hydrogen atom (Fig. 6-1). Therefore, we need only replace the quantum number $l$, which governs atomic electronic motion, by the quantum number $J$ for molecular rotational motion, and we know the necessary symmetry properties of rotational $\psi$-functions upon inversion. When $J$ is even, $\psi$ is $(g)$; when $J$ is odd, $\psi$ is $(u)$. Similar considerations apply to rotation of more complex diatomic molecules.

---

* It is proper to incorporate $g$-$u$ symmetry into the notation for atoms, although it is not usually used. See G. Herzberg's *Spectra of Diatomic Molecules*, 2nd ed. (Princeton: Van Nostrand), 1950, pp. 129, 318.

## SYMMETRY FOR HETERONUCLEAR DIATOMIC MOLECULES

The inversion operation *cannot* be performed on the electronic wave function, $\psi_{\text{elec}}$, for heteronuclear diatomic molecules, since inversion actually leads to a new function, and hence is not a symmetry operation. The reflection operation described above is the only one of importance for $\psi_{\text{elec}}$ of heteronuclear molecules.

For all molecules, the symmetries of rotational levels are governed by the symmetries of $\psi_{\text{total}}$, which is given by

$$\psi_{\text{total}} = \psi_{\text{rot}}\,\psi_{\text{elec}}. \tag{9-1}$$

As we have seen, $\psi_{\text{rot}}$ is $(g)$ or $(u)$; $\psi_{\text{elec}}$ is $(+)$ or $(-)$. The rules for their combination are

$$\begin{aligned}
(g) \times (+) &= (u) \times (-) = (+), \\
(g) \times (-) &= (u) \times (+) = (-).
\end{aligned} \tag{9-2}$$

When it is remembered that $(g)$ is analogous to $(+)$ and $(u)$ to $(-)$, then these rules are easy to remember. It follows that the rotational levels are $(+)$ for even $J$ and $(-)$ for odd $J$, provided that $\psi_{\text{elec}}$ is $(+)$. However, if $\psi_{\text{elec}}$ is $(-)$, then odd-numbered $J$-levels have $(+)$ symmetry and even-numbered $J$-levels have $(-)$ symmetry. These results are summarized for rigid-rotor $(^1\Sigma)$ molecules (Fig. 9–2a); for symmetric-top $(^1\Pi$ and $^1\Delta)$ molecules (Fig. 9–2b); and for Hund's case (a) and case (b) molecules (Figs. 9–2c, d, respectively). In these diagrams, the spacing of the rotational levels and sublevels is arbitrary.

Figure 9–2(b), for heteronuclear symmetric tops, summarizes the results of effects due to $\Lambda$, the component of the electronic orbital angular-momentum along the internuclear axis (cf. Chapters 7 and 8). Because $J$ must be greater than or equal to $\Lambda$, the $J = 0$ level does not exist for the $^1\Pi$-state $(\Lambda = 1)$, and the $J = 0$ and $J = 1$ levels do not exist for the $^1\Delta$-state $(\Lambda = 2)$. A doubling of the $J$-levels is noted and is called $\Lambda$-doubling. Usually the splitting is so small that it can be neglected so far as rotational energies are concerned. An exception occurs for the diatomic hydrides. However, two rotational sublevels always exist for each value of $J$ for $^1\Pi$- and $^1\Delta$-states, whether or not they are of identical energy. Furthermore, the sublevels have opposite symmetries because $M_L$, obtained from the component of $\mathbf{L}$, can be either positive or negative. Also, $\psi_{\text{elec}}$ is $(+)$ if $M_L$ is $(+)$, and $\psi_{\text{elec}}$ is $(-)$ if $M_L$ is $(-)$; hence the change in symmetry for the two sublevels. This means that there is a 50-50 chance of the motion of the electrons being in one sense or in the opposite sense about the internuclear axis. In other words, left-handed or right-handed molecules are equally probable.

The cause of $\Lambda$-doubling is interaction of the net orbital electron motion with the rotational motion of the internuclear axis. Lambda-doubling is a subtle effect, which, as a good approximation (with the exception of hydrides),

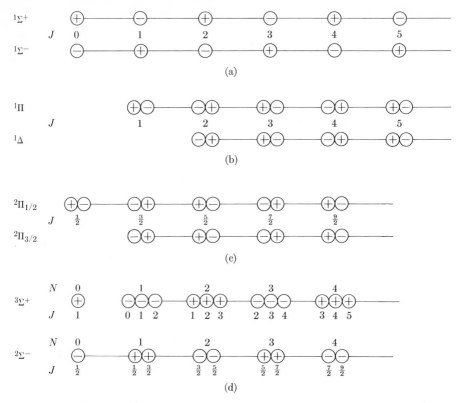

**Fig. 9–2.** Symmetry properties of rotational levels for heteronuclear diatomic molecules. The spacing of levels is arbitrary. (a) Rigid rotor molecules. (b) Symmetric top molecules. The splitting of rotational levels, except for hydrides, is usually negligible. (c) Examples of Hund's case (a) molecules. Again, the splitting of levels is often negligible. (d) Examples of Hund's case (b) molecules. The splitting of $^2\Sigma$-levels is given by Eqs. (8–10) and (8–11).

can be neglected in performing a spectral analysis, particularly for small $J$. However, when it is properly taken into account, it shows clearly the opposite symmetries of the rotational sublevels.

For Hund's case (a), $\Omega$ replaces $\Lambda$ for a symmetric top. Levels of $J$ less than the value of $\Omega$ are not physically possible for Hund's case (a) molecules; for example, the $J = \frac{1}{2}$ level is missing when $\Omega = \frac{3}{2}$. For a $^2\Pi$-state, the two components $^2\Pi_{1/2}$ and $^2\Pi_{3/2}$ behave like completely independent states. It should perhaps be emphasized that these two components result from the interaction of electronic spin with the magnetic field produced by the net orbital motion of the electrons about the internuclear axis (see Eq. 8–9). The splitting between the two states increases with increasing molecular weight.

## SYMMETRY FOR HOMONUCLEAR DIATOMIC MOLECULES

All of the elements of symmetry, described above for heteronuclear molecules also apply to homonuclear molecules. In addition, because the two nuclei are identical, an additional degree of symmetry is introduced. The inversion operation is now applicable to $\psi_{elec}$. Upon inversion, the electronic wave function either retains its original sign, in which case it is designated $(g)$, or it changes sign and is given the symbol $(u)$, as shown in Figs. 7–1 and 7–2. The new element of symmetry also has an effect on $\psi_{total}$ (Eq. 9–1). The rules for determining the effect are

$$(g) \times (g) = (u) \times (u) = (s),$$
$$(g) \times (u) = (u) \times (g) = (a), \tag{9-3}$$

where $(s)$ stands for symmetric and $(a)$ for antisymmetric. When it is remembered that $(g)$ and $(s)$ are analogous to $(+)$, and $(u)$ and $(a)$ to $(-)$, these rules are easy to remember. The $(s)$-$(a)$ notation is used to make it clear that a different combination of symmetry operations is involved, which is applicable to rotational levels of homonuclear diatomic molecules only. These rules are illustrated in Fig. 9–3 for some typical molecular states.

The reflection operation is still applicable to $\psi_{elec}$, and the rules for determining the sign of $\psi_{total}$ still apply in the same way as for heteronuclear molecules. The difference for rotational levels of homonuclear molecules is that $(s)$- or $(a)$-symmetry must be considered, *as well as* $(+)$- or $(-)$-symmetry.

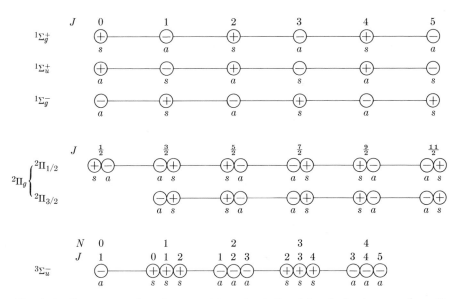

**Fig. 9–3.** Some examples of symmetries of rotational levels for homonuclear diatomic molecules. The spacing of levels is arbitrary.

## SELECTION RULES

Whether or not a transition from a molecular state $n$ to a molecular state $m$ of higher energy can occur is determined by the *transition moment*, $P_{nm}$, given by

$$P_{nm} = \int \psi_n^* \Sigma e\mathbf{r}_i \psi_m \, d\tau, \qquad (9\text{--}4)$$

where $\psi_n^*$ is the wave equation for state $n$, $\psi_m$ is the wave equation for state $m$, $\Sigma e\mathbf{r}_i$ represents electric vectors which are averaged over the two states and determined by the influence of the strong electric field along the internuclear axis on the $i$ electrons, and $d\tau$ is an element of volume.*

If any of these factors within the integral vanishes, then the transition moment is zero, and thus the transition is forbidden. From the few forms of Eq. (9–4), where $P_{nm}$ is finite, the *selection rules* for allowed transitions are deduced. For a single electronic state $\Sigma e\mathbf{r}_i$ is simply the permanent dipole moment of the molecule, and therefore rotational and vibrational transitions are forbidden for molecules with no permanent dipole. However, $\Sigma e\mathbf{r}_i$ over two different electronic states of the same molecule is not zero. The wave functions are conveniently expressed in the form of determinants, which are often equal to zero because of symmetry elements. All selection rules can in principle be derived from Eq. (9–4), whether they might otherwise be conveniently discussed in terms of conservation of angular momentum or in terms of symmetry.

For electronic transitions, the major rules are $\Delta S = 0$; $\Delta \Lambda = 0, \pm 1$; $+ \leftrightarrow +$, $- \leftrightarrow -$, and $g \leftrightarrow u$. The rules for $\Delta S$ and $\Delta \Lambda$ can be discussed in terms of conservation of angular momentum, as was the rule for rotational transitions, $\Delta J = \pm 1$, and, in certain cases, $\Delta J = 0, \pm 1$. The rule $\Delta S = 0$ is rigorous only for the four molecular models we have considered here. For increasing molecular weight, $S$ begins to lose its physical significance, as individual spin and orbital motions tend to couple. The coupling produces a torque which enables the electron to change spin slowly. For most molecules, very weak transitions corresponding to $\Delta S = 1$ have been observed and are called *intersystem crossings*. For very heavy atoms and molecules, the intersystem crossings are strongly allowed. Radiationless transitions in which $\Delta S = 1$ are facilitated by collisional processes. However, we shall not discuss violations of the rule $\Delta S = 0$ further here. The double arrows, for example, in the rule $g \leftrightarrow u$, simply mean it does not matter whether the transition occurs in emission or absorption, provided that one state is ($g$) and the other is ($u$). The (+)-(−) symmetry for electronic states is specifically designated as such for $\Sigma$-states, by a superscript after the $\Sigma$. The (+)-(−) symmetry is also applicable to $\Pi$- and $\Delta$-states, although it is not designated as such, since both symmetries occur as inseparable pairs. A study of the

---

* The wave function $\psi^*$ is a complex conjugate function, which means that everywhere $i$ occurs in the original $\psi$ function, it is replaced by $-i$.

symmetries of rotational levels of Π-states (also applicable to Δ-states) in Figs. 9–2 and 9–3 shows that the rule $\psi_{total} = \psi_{elec}\,\psi_{rot}$ must be applicable, with half the levels belonging to a $\psi_{elec}$, and hence $M_L$, which is $(+)$; and the other half to a $\psi_{elec}$ and $M_L$ which is $(-)$ (see p. 93). This, coupled with the usual alternation in sign for successive values of $J$ then accounts for the observed symmetries of rotational levels of Π- and Δ-states.

For vibration-rotation spectra, the selection rule $\Delta v = 1$ is rigorous for the harmonic-oscillator model. For real molecules, however, weak infrared spectra corresponding to $\Delta v \geq 2$ are observed, and for electronic transitions there is no restriction on $\Delta v$, other than that imposed by the Franck-Condon principle.

For transitions between *rotational* levels, whether of the same or different electronic states, the rules are $\Delta J = \pm 1$ or $\Delta J = 0, \pm 1; + \leftrightarrow -; s \leftrightarrow s,$ $a \leftrightarrow a$. It should be emphasized that these are applicable to the total resultant molecular rotation, the symmetry of which is determined by the product of $\psi_{elec}\,\psi_{rot}$. Thus the rotational $+ \leftrightarrow -$ rule is directly applicable to the levels for both homonuclear and heteronuclear molecules, indicated in Figs. 9–2 and 9–3, and the $s \leftrightarrow s, a \leftrightarrow a$ rules are applicable to the levels for homonuclear molecules in Fig. 9–3.

## SPONTANEOUS AND STIMULATED EMISSION

Since the equation for obtaining transition moments has been introduced, we digress momentarily to discuss some other important applications.

Another important property of Eq. (9–4) is that it can be written as

$$P_{nm} = P_{mn} = \int \psi_m^* \Sigma e\mathbf{r}_i \psi_n \, d\tau, \tag{9-5}$$

so that the transition moment is the same for emission or absorption. One state of the system might be said to be perturbed by the other state, and the mutual perturbations are identical in magnitude. The rate of change of light intensity is given by

$$\frac{dI}{dt} = AN_m + BI(N_m - N_n), \tag{9-6}$$

where $I$ is the light intensity, $N_m$ and $N_n$ are the number of molecules in states $m$ and $n$, $A$ is the Einstein coefficient of spontaneous emission, and $B$ is the Einstein coefficient of stimulated emission. If $I$ is zero, there can be no stimulated emission, but spontaneous emission can still occur. The term $B$ is given by

$$B = \frac{8\pi^3}{3h^2} P^2, \tag{9-7}$$

where $P$ is the transition moment, with the subscripts omitted, since they are interchangeable. Normally a Boltzmann distribution exists whereby

$$N_m = N_n e^{-h\nu/kT}, \tag{9-8}$$

where $h\nu$ is the energy difference between states $m$ and $n$. For a steady state the light intensity is given by the formula for a blackbody radiator:

$$I = \frac{8\pi h\nu^3 c^3}{e^{h\nu/kT} - 1}. \tag{9-9}$$

Furthermore, for a steady state, $dI/dt = 0$ in Eq. (9-6). The combination of the results for Eqs. (9-6) to (9-9) leads to

$$A/B = 8\pi h\nu^3 c^3. \tag{9-10}$$

If $\nu$ is small, then stimulated emission prevails over spontaneous emission. If a population inversion can be induced, so that $N_m > N_n$ in Eq. (9-6), then conditions exist for maser or laser action.

The integral (9-5) can be expressed in terms of three separate coordinates, and the factor $\Sigma er_i$ may be different for different coordinates. Thus for certain transitions, emission of plane-polarized light is predicted, and it has been verified by experiment.

### ROTATIONAL STRUCTURE OF ALLOWED ELECTRONIC TRANSITIONS

We now have sufficient information to predict whether a given transition can occur, and if it can, the number of branches present in the observed bands. The first consideration necessary is whether any of the electronic selection rules $\Delta S = 0$; $\Delta \Lambda = 0$, $\pm 1$; $+ \leftrightarrow +$, $- \leftrightarrow -$; $g \leftrightarrow u$ is violated. The $+ \leftrightarrow +$, $- \leftrightarrow -$ rule is of direct concern only for $\Sigma$-states. Because of the doubling of levels for $\Pi$-, $\Delta$-states, so that plus and minus levels always occur in pairs, the $+ \leftrightarrow +$, $- \leftrightarrow -$ rule never prevents a transition involving a $\Pi$- or $\Delta$-state, but the $(+)$ or $(-)$ electronic symmetry affects the sign of the rotational levels and hence the form of the observed spectrum (for example, see Fig. 9-5). The $g \leftrightarrow u$ rule is only applicable to homonuclear molecules.

If none of the appropriate electronic selection rules is violated, then the next concern is the rotational selection rules $\Delta J = \pm 1$ or $\Delta J = 0$, $\pm 1$; $+ \leftrightarrow -$; $s \leftrightarrow s$, $a \leftrightarrow a$; the latter pair of rules again are only of concern for homonuclear molecules. We shall now discuss specific examples of electronic transitions.

**Singlet-singlet transitions;** $^1\Sigma^+ - {}^1\Sigma^+$. Allowed electronic transitions between $^1\Sigma$-states are $^1\Sigma^+ \leftrightarrow {}^1\Sigma^+$ and $^1\Sigma^- \leftrightarrow {}^1\Sigma^-$ for heteronuclear molecules and $^1\Sigma_g^+ \leftrightarrow {}^1\Sigma_u^+$, $^1\Sigma_g^- \leftrightarrow {}^1\Sigma_u^-$ for homonuclear molecules. The symmetries of both sets of rotational levels, discussed individually previously, are shown together in Fig. 9-4(a). From the application of the rotational selection rules

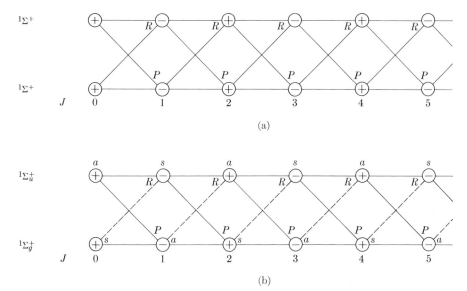

**Fig. 9-4.** $^1\Sigma \leftrightarrow {}^1\Sigma$ transitions. (a) $^1\Sigma^+ - {}^1\Sigma^+$. (b) $^1\Sigma_u^+ - {}^1\Sigma_g^+$. The values given for $J$ refer to the upper as well as the lower state. In (b) the transitions between the symmetric levels are indicated by broken lines, although in certain cases it is the antisymmetric transitions which are weak or missing. Adapted from G. Herzberg, *Spectra of Diatomic Molecules*, 2nd ed., (Princeton: Van Nostrand) 1950.

$+ \leftrightarrow -$, $\Delta J = \pm 1$, it can be seen that the $R$-branch lines are represented as lines of positive slope, and the $P$-branch lines as lines of negative slope. It can also be seen that the selection rule $\Delta J = \pm 1$ for rigid rotors is compatible with the rotational symmetry selection rule $+ \leftrightarrow -$. The $^1\Sigma^- \leftrightarrow {}^1\Sigma^-$ transition would be identical in form, since the change in symmetry of all levels would not affect either of the rules $+ \leftrightarrow -$ or $\Delta J = \pm 1$. It would not be possible, therefore, to tell from a $^1\Sigma - {}^1\Sigma$ transition alone, whether both electronic states are $(+)$ or both are $(-)$, although examples of the latter are rare, and are unknown for ground-state molecules.

For homonuclear $^1\Sigma^+$-molecules, the additional $g$- or $u$-element of symmetry would not be expected to cause any further simplification of the observed spectrum, since the selection rules $s \leftrightarrow s$, $a \leftrightarrow a$, are not violated for the transitions which obey the rules $+ \leftrightarrow -$, and $\Delta J = \pm 1$. However, an unexpected result is observed in that alternate lines in each branch are weak, or entirely missing. This result is represented schematically in Fig. 9-4(b). This weakness made dubious the validity of either the $a \leftrightarrow a$ or $s \leftrightarrow s$ selection rule, depending on the particular molecule, for homonuclear $^1\Sigma^+ - {}^1\Sigma^+$ transitions. This puzzling result was not clarified until the theory of nuclear spins was taken into account (see Chapter 10).

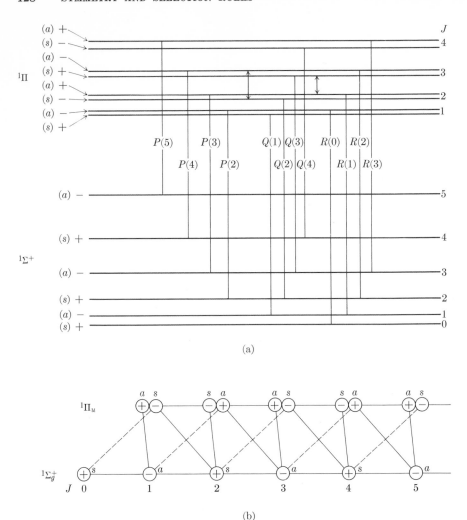

(a)

(b)

**Fig. 9-5.** (a) Energy-level diagram for the first lines of a $^1\Pi-^1\Sigma^+$ transition. For the sake of clarity, the $\Lambda$-type doubling in the $^1\Pi$-state has been greatly exaggerated. The double arrow to the left in (a) gives $R(2) - Q(2)$, and the one to the right gives $Q(3) - P(3)$. Their difference gives the sum of the $\Lambda$-doublings for $J = 2$ and $J = 3$ in the upper state. The designations $s$ and $a$, added in parentheses, hold for a $^1\Pi_u-^1\Sigma_g$ transition for identical nuclei. [Adapted from G. Herzberg, *Spectra of Diatomic Molecules*, 2nd Ed. (Princeton: Van Nostrand), 1950.] (b) $^1\Pi_u-\Sigma_g^+$ transition. We have shown the symmetric transitions as dashed lines, though it may be, in certain cases, that the antisymmetric transitions are weak or missing.

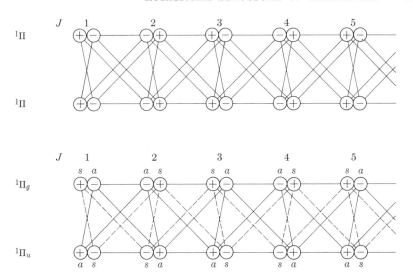

**Fig. 9-6.**   (a) $^1\Pi-^1\Pi$ transitions.   (b) $^1\Pi_g-^1\Pi_u$ transitions.   In all cases the $P$-lines slope to the left, $R$-lines slope to the right, and the $Q$-lines are roughly vertical  Note that all lines are doubled, provided that the $\Lambda$-doubling is apparent. For the homonuclear $^1\Pi$-states, part (b), the $s \leftrightarrow s$ transitions are shown as dashed lines, although, for certain cases, it is the $a \leftrightarrow a$ transitions which are weak or missing.

$^1\Pi-^1\Sigma^+$.   From a study of Fig. 9-5(a) we see that the selection rule $\Delta J = 0$, $\pm 1$, which we deduced from the experiment for a symmetric top, also applies to transitions from a rigid rotor to a symmetric top.  The transitions corresponding to $\Delta J = 0$ correspond to the $Q$-branch.  One can deduce that interchange of the upper and lower electronic states, or interchange of a $^1\Sigma$-state for $^1\Sigma^+$, does not affect the form of the observed spectrum, provided that the two components of each $\Pi$-state rotational level are of identical energy.  This is true to a good approximation, and we shall not consider until later the slight splitting of these levels which becomes apparent at high $J$ or very high resolution.  This splitting occurs particularly in hydride molecules and is due to $\Lambda$-doubling.

As an example of a homonuclear $^1\Pi-^1\Sigma$ transition, we shall consider the case $^1\Pi_u \leftarrow {}^1\Sigma_g^+$ (Fig. 9-5b).  It can be seen that no change is introduced in the observed spectrum by the $(s)$-$(a)$ symmetry, except for a diminution of either the $a \leftrightarrow a$ or $s \leftrightarrow s$ transitions, which was discussed under $^1\Sigma_g^+-^1\Sigma_u^+$ transitions.

$^1\Pi-^1\Pi$.   All $P$-, $Q$-, and $R$-branches are doubled if the $\Lambda$-doubling is apparent (Fig. 9-6).  For a $^1\Pi_g-^1\Pi_u$ transition—involving, of course, homonuclear molecules (Fig. 9-6b)—again either the $a \leftrightarrow a$ or $s \leftrightarrow s$ transitions are weak or missing.

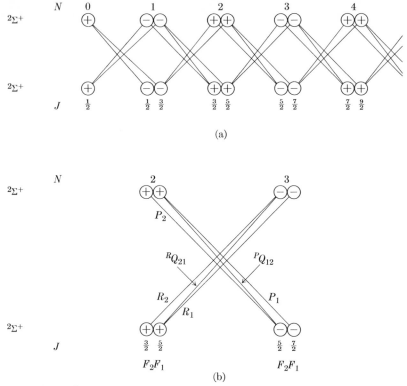

**Fig. 9-7.** $^2\Sigma^+-^2\Sigma^+$ transition. Part (b) is an enlargement of a portion of part (a). In part (b) $F_2$ and $F_1$ have the same meaning they had in Eq. (8–10) and (8–11) The $P_2$-line occurs between $F_2$-levels; similarly the $P_1$-line occurs between $F_1$-levels. The $^PQ_{12}$-line ($P$-form $Q$-line) behaves like a $P$-line, although it obeys the rule $\Delta J = 0$. The subscript 12 in $^PQ_{12}$ describes an $F_1 - F_2$ transition.

**Doublet-doublet transitions;** $^2\Sigma^+ \leftrightarrow {}^2\Sigma^+$. For this transition, we need a new selection rule, $\Delta N = \pm1$. For a $\Sigma$-state, $N$ is the total angular momentum apart from spin; thus for a $^2\Sigma$-state, $J = N \pm \frac{1}{2}$ (see Fig. 8–8). We see in Fig. 9–7 that the rule $+ \leftrightarrow -$ results in a total of six branches. However, if the doublet splitting is negligible, each of three pairs of branches coalesce into single branches, and the spectrum appears as that of a simple $P$- and $R$-branch. Under high resolution and for sufficiently high $J$, the splitting does become apparent, however. Consider the enlargement of a part of Fig. 9–7(a), which is shown in Fig. 9–7(b) (see also Eq. 8–10 and 8–11). For our purposes, it will suffice to state that observation of the six branches under high resolution provides convincing proof that a transition between multiplet $\Sigma$-states is occurring, and the average spacing of the apparent $P$- and $R$-branch lines observed under low resolution (each of which has three components) is satisfactory to obtain rotational constants of upper and lower states.

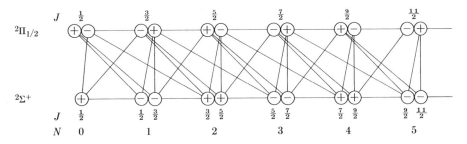

**Fig. 9-8.**  $^2\Pi_{1/2}-^2\Sigma$ transitions. Note that by using the rotational selection rules $\Delta J = 0, \pm 1, + \leftrightarrow -$, it can be shown that there are two $P$-, two $Q$-, and two $R$-branches, for a total of six branches for the $^2\Pi_{1/2}-^2\Sigma$ transition.

The effect of the additional symmetry for homonuclear $^2\Sigma$-states is the same in principle as that for $^1\Sigma$-states. For $^2\Sigma_g \leftrightarrow ^2\Sigma_u$ transitions, where only two apparent branches are observed under lower resolution, the same peculiar intensity alternation is observed for homonuclear molecules as it is for the corresponding $^1\Sigma_g \leftrightarrow ^1\Sigma_u$ transitions. Doublet-doublet homonuclear transitions can occur for ionic species only.

$^2\Pi-^2\Sigma$.  We assume that the $^2\Pi$-state belongs to Hund's case (a). A total of six branches occur (Fig. 9-8). The same considerations apply to a $^2\Pi_{3/2}-^2\Sigma^+$ transition as to a $^2\Pi_{1/2}-^2\Sigma^+$ transition, except that in the former case the $J = \frac{1}{2}$ level for the $^2\Pi_{3/2}$-state does not exist.

$^2\Pi-^2\Pi$.  Two distinct bands are observed, $^2\Pi_{3/2}-^2\Pi_{3/2}$ and $^2\Pi_{1/2}-^2\Pi_{1/2}$. There is a selection rule $\Delta\Omega = 0$, so that the transitions $^2\Pi_{3/2} \leftrightarrow ^2\Pi_{1/2}$ are forbidden. This simplifies the observed spectrum. A schematic representation of a $^2\Pi_{1/2}-^2\Pi_{1/2}$ transition is shown in Fig. 9-9. In principle, there is no difference between a vibration-rotation band and an electronic band; as a practical example of a $^2\Pi-^2\Pi$ transition, see the i.r. band for the $1 \leftarrow 0$, $^2\Pi-^2\Pi$ transition of nitric oxide in Fig. 8-4. Note the $Q$-branch lines, which are superimposed, and note also the line doubling, which becomes apparent for large rotational quantum numbers, due to the superposition of spectra for the $^2\Pi_{1/2} \leftarrow ^2\Pi_{1/2}$ and $^2\Pi_{3/2} \leftarrow ^2\Pi_{3/2}$ transitions.

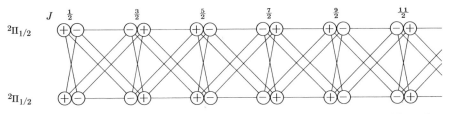

**Fig. 9-9.**  $^2\Pi_{1/2}-^2\Pi_{1/2}$ transitions. Note that there are two closely spaced branches for each of the designations $P$, $Q$, and $R$.

**Fig. 9-10.** Fine structure of the AlH band at 4241 Å. The band is degraded to the red. Note the second band head caused by the Q-branch. This spectrum was obtained in the undergraduate physical chemistry laboratory at the University College, University of London. We are indebted to Dr. John Callomon for the film.

### SPECTRAL ANALYSIS WHEN Λ-DOUBLING IS IMPORTANT

In Chapter 8 we discussed the procedure to be followed for the analysis of a band which contains P-, Q-, and R- branches, without the complication of appreciable splitting due to Λ-doubling. The importance of Λ-doubling on symmetry properties of rotational sublevels has been discussed in some detail above. Its effect in causing an appreciable splitting of rotational levels is usually only important for molecules with large $B_v$ values, such as the hydrides. The effect of Λ-doubling is shown schematically in Fig. 9–5(a) for $^1\Pi \to {}^1\Sigma^+$ bands, of which AlH provides an example. A plate of part of the AlH spectrum is shown in Fig. 9–10. It can be seen in Fig. 9–5 that the P- and R-branches involve only the upper rotational sublevels of the $^1\Pi$-state, whereas the Q-branch involves the lower rotational sublevels of the $^1\Pi$-state. The combination differences, $\Delta_2 F(J)$, for the P- and R-branches, can be used to obtain precise B-values for upper and lower electronic states. However, the $\Delta_1 F(J)$ values exhibit peculiar behavior, because they involve the splitting of the upper-state levels, $\varepsilon$, which increases with increasing $J$. Thus

$$\Delta_1 F(J') = R(J) - Q(J) = Q(J+1) - P(J+1) + \varepsilon, \quad (9\text{–}11)$$

$$\Delta_1 F(J'') = R(J) - Q(J+1) = Q(J) - P(J+1) + \varepsilon. \quad (9\text{–}12)$$

The splitting constant $\varepsilon$ is determined by means of these two equations. It can be seen that the $+ \leftrightarrow -$ rotational selection rule prevents the doubling of the three observed branches.

### PROBLEMS

1. Which of the following electronic transitions are not allowed? Which rules are violated?

   a) $^1\Sigma^+ - {}^1\Sigma^-$      b) $^3\Sigma^+ - {}^1\Sigma^+$      c) $^3\Delta_u - {}^1\Sigma_u$

   d) $^1\Pi_g - {}^1\Sigma_u$      e) $^2\Pi_{3/2} - {}^2\Pi_{1/2}$

2. Which of the following electronic transitions are allowed? List all selection rules which are obeyed.

   a) $^1\Sigma_u^+ - {}^1\Sigma_g^+$      b) $^1\Sigma_u^- - {}^1\Sigma_u^+$      c) $^3\Delta_u - {}^3\Pi_g$

   d) $^2\Sigma_u^+ - {}^2\Sigma_g^+$      e) $^1\Sigma_u^+ - {}^3\Sigma_g^-$      f) $^1\Pi - {}^1\Sigma$

   g) $^2\Pi - {}^2\Delta$

3. A transition is described as $^2\Sigma_g \leftarrow {}^2\Sigma_u$ for an uncharged, homonuclear, diatomic molecule. What is obviously wrong with this statement?

4. Construct an energy-level diagram for a band of a $^1\Pi \leftrightarrow {}^1\Sigma^+$ transition. Indicate the symmetries and $J$-values of all rotational levels. What are the first lines of each branch? Assuming that the splitting due to $\Lambda$-doubling is negligible, is it possible to distinguish this transition from a $^1\Pi \leftrightarrow {}^1\Sigma^-$ transition? Why?

5. Indicate the $J$-values, and where appropriate, $N$-values, and symmetries of the first few rotational levels of each of the following electronic states.

   a) $^1\Sigma_u^-$         b) $^2\Pi_u$         c) $^3\Sigma^+$
   d) $^3\Pi$              e) $^3\Sigma_g^+$         f) $^2\Sigma_g^-$

6. Discuss whether you could distinguish

   a) a $^1\Pi_u \leftarrow {}^1\Sigma_g^+$ transition from a $^1\Sigma_g^+ \leftarrow {}^1\Pi_u$ transition;
   b) $^1\Pi_g \leftarrow {}^1\Sigma_u^+$ from $^1\Pi_u \leftarrow {}^1\Sigma_g^+$.

   Do not discuss any possible intensity alternation due to nuclear spin at this stage.

7. Outline the difference, if any, under high resolution, between $^2\Sigma^+ \leftarrow {}^2\Pi$ and $^2\Pi \leftarrow {}^2\Sigma^+$ transitions. Give reasons for your answer.

8. Sketch energy-level diagrams with all pertinent information, and show bands for the following transitions.

   a) $^1\Pi \leftarrow {}^1\Pi$         b) $^2\Pi - {}^2\Sigma$         c) $^2\Sigma_u^+ - {}^2\Sigma_g^+$
   d) $^1\Pi_u \leftarrow {}^1\Sigma_g^+$      e) $^3\Pi \leftarrow {}^3\Sigma^+$

   Ignore any effects due to nuclear spin.

9. The following data apply to the $^1\Pi \rightarrow {}^1\Sigma$ transition in AlH. Devise two ways to compute the value of $\mathcal{E}$, the magnitude of which indicates the extent of splitting of levels due to $\Lambda$-doubling.

$$cm^{-1}$$

| $J$ | $R(J)$ | $Q(J)$ | $P(J)$ |
|---|---|---|---|
| 0 | 23,483.54 | | |
| 1 | 494.36 | 23,470.20 | |
| 2 | 505.18 | 469.07 | 23,445.06 |
| 3 | 515.46 | 467.33 | 431.42 |
| 4 | 525.09 | 464.96 | 417.09 |
| 5 | 534.00 | 462.03 | 402.31 |

10. Discuss the similarities and differences of the selection rules for (a) $\Delta J = \pm 1$, compared to $+ \leftrightarrow -$ for rigid-rotor heteronuclear molecules; (b) $\Delta J = 0, \pm 1$, compared to $+ \leftrightarrow -$ for symmetric-top heteronuclear molecules.

11. Discuss whether the electronic selection rules, $+ \leftrightarrow +$, $- \leftrightarrow -$, can be derived solely on the basis of the rotational rules, $+ \leftrightarrow -$ and $\Delta J = \pm 1$.

## CHAPTER 10

# ELECTRON AND NUCLEAR SPIN; ENERGY LEVEL POPULATIONS

In Chapter 9 we saw that for some transitions involving homonuclear diatomic molecules, anomalous intensity distributions are observed in which certain branches are either absent or are much fainter than would be expected from the normal selection rules. We shall attempt to describe here the reason for this puzzling phenomenon and also to discuss the problem of population of energy levels in general.

## ELECTRON SPIN REVISITED

Before we discuss the influence of nuclear spin, which, it turns out, is responsible for the intensity alternation observed in spectra of homonuclear diatomic molecules, let us complete our discussion of electron spin, a closely related phenomenon. Consider the possible spin orientations of two electrons in two different orbitals:

$$\alpha(1)\alpha(2),$$
$$\alpha(1)\beta(2),$$
$$\beta(1)\alpha(2),$$
$$\beta(1)\beta(2).$$

$$(10\text{--}1)$$

The symbols $\alpha$ and $\beta$ are used to designate spins of $+\frac{1}{2}$ and $-\frac{1}{2}$, respectively, and the symbols (1) and (2) to label the two electrons. In reality, there is of course no way of distinguishing the two electrons, and this must be taken into account for a proper spin wave function. The spin function must have the usual property of being symmetric or antisymmetric, but it must also recognize the fact that the two electrons cannot be distinguished. The $\alpha(1)\alpha(2)$ and $\beta(1)\beta(2)$ functions are satisfactory according to both criteria. Exchange of the two electrons causes no change in the total spin wave functions, which are therefore symmetric; and the function does not attempt to distinguish the two electrons, since they both have spin $m_s = +\frac{1}{2}$ or $-\frac{1}{2}$. In other words, a function such as $\alpha(1)\alpha(2)$ is in no way different from the function $\alpha(2)\alpha(1)$.

The two functions, $\alpha(1)\beta(2)$ and $\beta(1)\alpha(2)$, are improper, however, because they state that it is known which electron has spin $m_s = +\frac{1}{2}$ and which one has $m_s = -\frac{1}{2}$. A linear combination of two functions resolves the difficulty:*

$$\alpha(1)\beta(2) + \beta(1)\alpha(2), \qquad (10\text{--}2)$$

$$\alpha(1)\beta(2) - \beta(1)\alpha(2). \qquad (10\text{--}3)$$

For Eq. (10–2), the interchange of the numbers (1) and (2) leads to the function

$$\alpha(2)\beta(1) + \beta(2)\alpha(1), \qquad (10\text{--}4)$$

which is completely equivalent to Eq. (10–2), and is therefore a symmetric function. Equation (10–3), upon exchange, becomes

$$\alpha(2)\beta(1) - \beta(2)\alpha(1), \qquad (10\text{--}5)$$

which is Eq. (10–3) multiplied by $-1$. Equation (10–3) is therefore antisymmetric.

The resultant proper wave equations are therefore

$$
\left.
\begin{aligned}
&\alpha(1)\alpha(2), \\
&\alpha(1)\beta(2) + \beta(1)\alpha(2), \\
&\beta(1)\beta(2),
\end{aligned}
\right\} \text{symmetric;} \qquad (10\text{--}6)
$$

$$\alpha(1)\beta(2) - \beta(1)\alpha(2), \qquad \text{antisymmetric.} \qquad (10\text{--}7)$$

The three triplet functions are sometimes represented as ↑↑, ↑↓, and ↓↓, and the singlet function as ↓↑, which gives the proper statistical weight, but, as we intimated in Chapter 6, there is an ambiguity with respect to the two apparently equivalent configurations, ↑↓ and ↓↑. From Eqs. (10–6) and (10–7), the nature of this ambiguity now becomes more clear. Instead of using the notation ↑↓ for one component of the triplet, we should use the symmetric notation, (↑↓) + (↓↑), and instead of the notation ↓↑ for the singlet, we should use the antisymmetric notation, (↑↓) − (↓↑). The shorthand notation ↑↑ is satisfactory for the three components of the triplet, provided it is understood that the notation represents the three symmetric spin functions in Eq. (10–6). For the singlet state, the shorthand notation ↓↑ is satisfactory, provided it is understood that the notation represents the antisymmetric spin function in Eq. (10–7).

Electrons, like all other particles with half-integral spins, are sometimes called fermions, since they obey Fermi-Dirac statistics. In these statistics, the total wave function must always be antisymmetric with respect to exchange of particles. This is the most general formulation of the Pauli principle. We discussed above the symmetry of the electron spin wave functions. We must now take into account the symmetry of the electron orbital

---

* Any linear combination which yields orthogonal functions is satisfactory. The above linear combinations are the simplest and therefore are commonly used.

wave function, which also contributes to the total *electronic* wave function for the two-electron system. For the triplet state, the spin wave function is symmetric. Since $(a) \times (s) = (a)$, it follows that the corresponding orbital wave function must be antisymmetric. On the other hand, since the spin wave function for the singlet state is antisymmetric, it follows that the orbital wave function for this state must be symmetric. This expresses the fact that triplet and singlet states, which involve the same two orbitals and naïvely might be expected to be equivalent, have different wave functions, and hence different spatial distributions of their electron clouds. Two electrons which form a triplet state tend to avoid each other, since they have the same spins; and hence, because they are usually far apart, the average electrostatic repulsion is low. On the other hand, two electrons which form a singlet state of the same m.o. configuration as that of the triplet can closely approach each other, since they have opposite spins, and the average electrostatic repulsion is higher than that for the corresponding triplet.* The difference in energy is not caused directly by the spin-spin interactions, which are known to be weak. Rather, the difference in energy is an indirect result of electron spin, which enhances or diminishes the probability that two electrons can approach closely.

The case of *equivalent* singlet and triplet configurations, discussed above, refers to atoms or to molecules which have closed subshells. The case where the two highest energy orbitals are degenerate is illustrated in Fig. 10–1(a); the nondegenerate case is shown in Fig. 10–1(b).

For the particular case of the hydrogen molecule, where only two electrons are present, the triplet and singlet states which are formed upon the approach of two hydrogen atoms have *different* configurations. For the triplet state, there is one bonding and one antibonding electron, and the effect of the latter is predominant. This corresponds to the repulsive curve in Fig. 4–1. The singlet state corresponds to the bonding curve in Fig. 4–1. Both the singlet and triplet states of hydrogen are represented in Fig. 10–1[c].

---

* Our discussion of electron distributions in singlet and triplet states, located in Chapters 6 and 10, has attempted to summarize the conventional wisdom. The Pauli principle prevents two electrons with the same spins from occupying the same orbital. It is accepted as obvious that two electrons with antiparallel spins in the same orbital will be closer together on the average than two electrons with parallel spins, which must from the Pauli principle occupy separate orbitals. It is also generally accepted that when two electrons occupy two different orbitals, the average inter-electron distance is greater for a triplet state than for the corresponding singlet state. This appears to provide a ready explanation for the experimental fact that triplet states have lower energies than the corresponding singlet states, and it has been confirmed in a simplified calculation. It turns out that electrons in the 1s2p triplet configuration for helium are *closer* together than electrons in the 1s2p singlet configuration and that there are other compensating factors to account for the lower energy of the triplet state. This result was obtained from unpublished work by R. P. Messner and F. W. Birss, who used an accurate Hartree-Fock calculation and a more exact calculation.

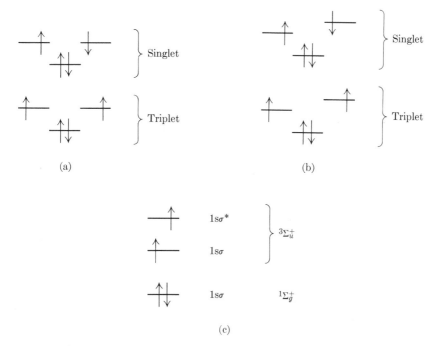

(a)                                                                      (b)

(c)

**Fig. 10-1.** Various effects of electron spin. (a) Singlet and triplet states of equivalent a.o. or m.o. configurations, involving degenerate orbitals. The triplet state is in this case a ground-state configuration. Only the three highest energy orbitals are shown. (b) Singlet and triplet states of equivalent a.o. or m.o. configurations, involving nondegenerate orbitals. Both configurations in this case represent excited states, although the triplet is of lower energy. (c) Singlet and triplet states of $H_2$, formed from ground-state atoms. The triplet state now has a different m.o. configuration than the singlet. Since the triplet is equivalent to no bonding electrons, it is of higher energy. Similar considerations apply to other singly bonded molecules.

## NUCLEAR SPIN

We can now return to the problem raised in Chapter 9 of why, for transitions involving homonuclear diatomic molecules, either the $(a)-(a)$ or $(s)-(s)$ transitions are weak or missing.

It turns out that most nuclei also have spin, designated by the quantum number, $I$. For protons, $I = \pm\frac{1}{2}$. Since protons, like electrons, have half-integral spins, they also obey Fermi-Dirac statistics. For molecules such as $H_2$, the result is that the total wave function, including nuclear spin, must always be antisymmetric:

$$\psi_{total} = \psi_{elec}\,\psi_{rot}\,\psi_{nuc}. \qquad (10\text{-}8)$$

Heteronuclear molecules need not be considered since the inversion operation, which determines the resultant symmetry, cannot be performed either on

$\psi_{\text{elec}}$ or the nuclear wave function, $\psi_{\text{nuc}}$. If it is performed, it leads to new $\psi$-functions, and hence is not a symmetry operation. As an example of the use of Eq. 10–8, $\psi_{\text{elec}}$ for the ground state of $H_2$ has $(g)$-symmetry; the even-numbered rotational wave functions are $(g)$ and the odd $(u)$; and, as described before, $(g) \times (g) = (s)$ and $(g) \times (u) = (a)$. Therefore the symmetry designation for $(\psi_{\text{elec}} \psi_{\text{rot}})$ is $(s)$ for even rotational levels and $(a)$ for odd rotational levels for ground-state $H_2$. The influence of $\psi_{\text{nuc}}$, specifically of the nuclear spin, is to determine the statistical weight of the $(s)$- and $(a)$-levels. Since $I = \pm\frac{1}{2}$ for a single proton, then the total spin for a pair of protons designated by $T$, will be 1 or 0. Three orientations correspond to $T = 1$, namely $\uparrow\uparrow$, $\uparrow\downarrow$, or $\downarrow\downarrow$; whereas for $T = 0$, there is only one possible orientation, $\downarrow\uparrow$. The statistical weight is therefore $3:1$ for the two cases $T = 1$ and $0$, respectively. The three orientations corresponding to $T = 1$ are symmetric in that if the two nuclei are exchanged (by inversion), no change in the associated spin wave function occurs. The single orientation $\downarrow\uparrow$, for the case where $T = 0$, is antisymmetric, since a change in sign in the associated spin wave function occurs upon exchange of the nuclei. The rule $(s) \times (a) = (a)$ and $(s) \times (s) = (a) \times (a) = (s)$ applies. Since, according to Fermi statistics, $\psi_{\text{total}}$ must always be antisymmetric, it follows that only $H_2$-molecules which have their nuclei in the triplet (symmetric) state, corresponding to $T = 1$, can populate the odd-numbered $(a)$ rotational levels, and only $H_2$-molecules which have their nuclei in the singlet (antisymmetric) state can populate the even-numbered $(s)$ rotational levels. Therefore, the statistical weight of odd- to even-numbered rotational levels in ground-state $H_2$ $(^1\Sigma_g^+)$ is $3:1$.

The hydrogen molecules which populate the odd-numbered $(a)$ rotational levels have been dubbed orthohydrogen, and those which populate the even-numbered $(s)$ levels are called parahydrogen. The selection rule $s \leftrightarrow s$, $a \leftrightarrow a$ is rigorous enough that the freezing of hydrogen will not readily convert orthohydrogen into parahydrogen, even though at temperatures below about $40°K$, the molecules would normally populate the $J = 0$ rotational level exclusively. The conversion is greatly facilitated, however, by paramagnetic substances such as nitric oxide and by activated charcoal. It is only in the case of hydrogen and its isotopes that nuclear spin affects markedly the bulk property of heat capacity.

Let us now consider the transition $^1\Sigma_u^+ - {}^1\Sigma_g^+$ for $H_2$ (the Lyman bands). The symmetries of the rotational levels are shown in Fig. 10–1(b). Since the upper state has $(u)$-symmetry, the even-numbered rotational levels are now $(a)$, and thus must have the greater statistical weight, since $H_2$-molecules whose nuclei are symmetric, that is, have $T = 1$, now occupy these levels. Therefore an inspection of Fig. 10–1(b) shows that in the resultant spectrum the $P$-branch has three times the intensity of the $R$-branch. This intensity rule ignores the Boltzmann factor, which will be discussed shortly.

Consider now the heavy hydrogen molecule, $D_2$. The deuterium nucleus, or deuteron, has spin $I = 0, \pm 1$. The resultant values of $T$ are therefore 2, 1, or 0, according to the usual rules of quantum vector addition; and the statistical weights, obtained from $2T + 1$, are $5:3:1$, respectively.* This means that the total statistical weight of molecules where the nuclei have an even (2 or 0) value of $T$ is twice as great as that for molecules where $T = 1$. The $D_2$-molecules, with even $T$, have symmetric nuclear spin wave functions; and those with odd $T$ have antisymmetric wave functions, as is shown below. In this respect, $D_2$ is no different from $H_2$ or any other homonuclear molecule.

Let us represent the spins of a deuteron as $\beta_{+1}$, $\beta_0$, and $\beta_{-1}$. Therefore, there are nine combinations possible for two deuterons, labeled (1) and (2):

$$\begin{array}{lll}
\beta_{+1}(1)\beta_{+1}(2), & \beta_0(1)\beta_0(2), & \beta_{-1}(1)\beta_{-1}(2), \\
\beta_{+1}(1)\beta_{-1}(2), & \beta_0(1)\beta_{+1}(2), & \beta_{-1}(1)\beta_0(2), \\
\beta_{-1}(1)\beta_{+1}(2), & \beta_{+1}(1)\beta_0(2), & \beta_0(1)\beta_{-1}(2).
\end{array} \qquad (10\text{--}9)$$

All these spin functions have the property of symmetry or antisymmetry, but only the top three are proper functions with regard to the fact that the two nuclei cannot be distinguished. The remaining six functions, in vertical pairs, can be made proper by linear combinations, such as

$$\begin{aligned}
&\beta_{+1}(1)\beta_{-1}(2) + \beta_{-1}(1)\beta_{+1}(2), \\
&\beta_{+1}(1)\beta_{-1}(2) - \beta_{-1}(1)\beta_{+1}(2),
\end{aligned} \qquad (10\text{--}10)$$

and so on. For the above pair of combinations, the first function is symmetric and the second, antisymmetric, with respect to exchange of the deuterons. The five spin functions which correspond to $T = 2$ are:

$$\begin{aligned}
&\beta_{+1}(1)\beta_{+1}(2), \\
&\beta_{+1}(1)\beta_0(2) + \beta_0(1)\beta_{+1}(2), \\
&\beta_0(1)\beta_0(2), \\
&\beta_{-1}(1)\beta_0(2) + \beta_0(1)\beta_{-1}(2), \\
&\beta_{-1}(1)\beta_{-1}(2).
\end{aligned} \qquad (10\text{--}11)$$

All of the above functions are symmetric. The three functions for $T = 1$ are the antisymmetric ones:

$$\begin{aligned}
&\beta_{+1}(1)\beta_0(2) - \beta_0(1)\beta_{+1}(2), \\
&\beta_{+1}(1)\beta_{-1}(2) - \beta_{-1}(1)\beta_{+1}(2), \\
&\beta_{-1}(1)\beta_0(2) - \beta_0(1)\beta_{-1}(2),
\end{aligned} \qquad (10\text{--}12)$$

---

* The multiplicity and corresponding statistical weight for a given spin configuration are equal. They are given by $2T + 1$ for nuclei and $2S + 1$ for electrons.

and for $T = 0$, we have the symmetric function

$$\beta_{+1}(1)\beta_{-1}(2) + \beta_{-1}(1)\beta_{+1}(2).$$

With no other knowledge of symmetry as applied to wave mechanics than has been outlined here, the correspondence of seven of the nine spin functions with their appropriate $T$-values is straightforward. So far, we have not sufficient knowledge to choose unambiguously whether the $\beta(1)\beta(2)$ function corresponds to $T = 0$, or whether it should be the middle of the five functions corresponding to $T = 2$. The latter five functions might be represented schematically as $\uparrow\uparrow$, $\uparrow\rightarrow$, $\leftarrow\rightarrow$, $\leftarrow\downarrow$, and $\downarrow\downarrow$; the three functions corresponding to $T = 1$, as $\leftarrow\uparrow$, $\leftarrow\rightarrow$, and $\uparrow\rightarrow$; and for $T = 0$, $\downarrow\uparrow$. These representations give the proper statistical weight. The simplest representations of the three allowed values of $T = 2$, 1, or 0 are $\uparrow\uparrow$, $\uparrow\rightarrow$, and $\uparrow\downarrow$ which, let us repeat, have statistical weights of $5:3:1$.

Deuterons, as well as all other particles with integral spins, are sometimes called bosons, since they obey Bose-Einstein statistics. For these statistics, the total wave function is symmetric. (Recall that the total wave function is antisymmetric for fermions.) For a $g$-state, the even-numbered $J$-levels are ($s$), and hence only bosons with even values of $T$, which are symmetric, can populate them; conversely, since the odd-numbered $J$-levels are ($a$), thus only bosons with odd values of $T$, which are antisymmetric, can populate them. This means, then that for deuterium in its electronic ground state, the even $J$-levels have twice the population that the odd levels have. This is in marked contrast to what is observed for $H_2$.

According to the above discussion, the population of rotational levels of a molecule, such as a HD or HT, is unaffected by the statistics of its component nuclei, since with unlike nuclei the crucial inversion symmetry element is lacking. This has been verified in experimental observations.

Finally, let us consider a molecule such as $O^{16}O^{16}$, where the nuclei have zero spin. Since $I = 0$, $T = 0$. Therefore all oxygen molecules have a symmetric nuclear spin function and obey Bose-Einstein statistics. This means that the antisymmetric rotational levels of $O^{16}O^{16}$ should not be populated at all, and this, in fact, is observed. It should be emphasized that Fermi and Bose statistics were originally developed on the basis of experimental spectral evidence.

Spins of several particles are summarized in Table 10–1. The spins of nuclei, of course, are responsible for the phenomenon of nuclear magnetic resonance. When a magnetic field of the correct or resonance frequency is applied to molecules which contain nuclei with spin, these spins will change their orientation, or "flip." The resonance frequency is a function not only of the spin of the nuclei, but also of the shielding of the nuclei by their electron environment. Therefore, when the spin of a given type of nucleus is known, fundamental information about the electron environment can be obtained.

**Table 10-1**

SPINS OF SOME PARTICLES IN UNITS OF $\hbar$

| Spin | Particles |
|---|---|
| 0 | $C^{12}$, $O^{16}$, $O^{18}$ |
| $\frac{1}{2}$ | $H^1$, $H^3$ or T, $C^{13}$, $N^{15}$, $F^{19}$, electrons, neutrons |
| 1 | $H^2$ or D, $N^{14}$, photons |
| $\frac{3}{2}$ | $Cl^{35}$ |
| $\frac{5}{2}$ | $O^{17}$, $I^{127}$ |
| 3 | B |

## BOLTZMANN FACTORS

So far, we have not discussed directly the effect of temperature on spectral intensity distributions, although in Chapter 5 the effect of temperature on vibrational energy-level populations was discussed. Qualitatively, it is easy to envisage that the higher the temperature, the greater will be the population of higher-energy levels, with a corresponding shift in spectral intensities. Quantitatively, correct intensities can be predicted in terms of the appropriate Boltzmann factors:

$$\frac{n_i}{n_0} = g_i e^{-\epsilon_i/kT}, \tag{5-4}$$

where $n_i/n_0$ is the ratio of molecules in the $i$th energy level to the total number of molecules in the zeroth energy level, $\epsilon_i$ is the energy of the $i$th level above the zeroth level, $k$ is the Boltzmann constant, $T$ is the absolute temperature, and $g_i$ is a statistical weight factor, which is used when there is some reason for weighting certain energy levels more than others. In other words, $g_i$ is not unity when the relative population of certain energy levels is not predicted by the simple exponential term.

## VIBRATIONAL ENERGIES

This is perhaps the simplest case to treat, since $g_i$ is unity. Vibrational populations were discussed in terms of bond-dissociation energies in Chapter 5.

## ROTATIONAL ENERGIES

We have seen that rotational wave functions are analogous to the angular part of electronic wave functions of the hydrogen atom. The latter have a $(2l + 1)$-degeneracy, and rotational levels have a $(2J + 1)$-degeneracy. Therefore, for heteronuclear molecules, $g_J = 2J + 1$. For homonuclear molecules, an additional factor must be superimposed to take into account the correct form of nuclear statistics. Thus for ground state $H_2$, the odd-numbered $J$-values have $g_J = 3(2J + 1)$ and the even-numbered ones have $g_J = 1(2J + 1)$. For rotational levels,

$$\epsilon_J = F(J) = B_v J(J + 1),$$

in wave number units.

For states with $\Lambda \neq 0$, the $\Lambda$-doubling is not a factor for all molecules where the levels are not split appreciably; rather it is a self-canceling factor, since it makes *all* levels of a given electronic state doubly degenerate. For multiplet $\Sigma$-states, the multiplicity affects the number of rotational levels, so that an appropriate factor is required.

## ELECTRONIC ENERGIES

A special weighting factor is required for multiplet states where $\Lambda \neq 0$. Thus for an excited $^3\Pi$-state, if $\epsilon_{elec}$ is large compared to the triplet splitting, then precise enough results are obtained simply by setting $g_{elec} = 3$ and assuming that $\epsilon_{elec}$ is constant for all three components of the $^3\Pi$-state. If, however, $\epsilon_{elec}$ is small compared to the triplet splitting, then each of the triplet components must be treated as a separate state, with $g_{elec} = 1$ for each component and $\epsilon_{elec}$ having a different value for each component, which takes into account the appropriate multiplet splitting. A combination of Boltzmann factors with selection rules enables one to predict relative line intensities. Care must be exercised for emission spectra, however, since the upper state may not be in thermal equilibrium, and Frank-Condon factors are likely to be more important.* Often the rotational levels of an electronic state attain thermal equilibrium rapidly and vibrational levels less rapidly. It is possible for a gas which is not at equilibrium to have different effective rotational, vibrational, and electronic temperatures.

## PROBLEMS

1. Two combining ground-state nitrogen atoms ($^4S$) form septet, quintet, triplet, and singlet $\Sigma$-states. Prove that the correct statistical weights for these states are $7:5:3:1$, respectively.

2. What are the relative populations of alternate rotational levels of the $^1\Sigma_g^+$-state of (a) $H_2$, (b) $D_2$? Disregard Boltzmann factors. Explain the rules which determine these relative populations.

3. Repeat Problem (2), but substitute $^1\Sigma_u^+$ for $^1\Sigma_g^+$.

---

* The intensities of lines for spontaneous emission are dependent on $\nu^3$ (see Chapter 9). However, for a u.v. spectrum, the relative changes in $\nu$ are small and as a first approximation can be neglected.

4. Construct schematic diagrams showing the intensity alternation of lines for the $^1\Sigma_u^+ - {}^1\Sigma_g^+$ transitions for both $H_2$ and $D_2$. State the precise relative intensities of lines, assuming that Boltzmann factors can be ignored.

5. What are the relative populations of alternate rotational levels of $^1\Sigma_g^+$-states for $B_2$, $O^{17}O^{17}$, $O^{16}O^{17}$? Why? Ignore Boltzmann factors. Repeat for $^1\Sigma_u^+$ and $^1\Sigma_g^-$ states.

6. Add to your answer for Problem 6, Chapter 8, a discussion of the behavior of bosons and fermions.

7. Reanswer Problems 8(c) and (d), Chapter 8, with a discussion of boson and fermion behavior.

8. For the ground state of $Br_2$, $\omega_e = 323.2$ and $\omega_e x_e = 1.07$ cm$^{-1}$. Compute the relative populations of the low-lying vibrational levels at 300°K, 1500°K.

9.

|  | HF | HCl | CO |
|---|---|---|---|
| $B_e$, cm$^{-1}$ | 20.94 | 10.59 | 1.977 |
| $\alpha_e$, cm$^{-1}$ | 0.77 | 0.30 | 0.019 |

Make use of the above rotational constants to plot $\exp\left[-B_v J(J+1)/kT\right]$ vs. $J$ at 300°K, 1000°K for the $v = 0$ level of the three molecules. Make sure your units are correct in the exponential term. (See Problem 17, Chapter 4, for the method of computation of $B_0$.) Superimpose a plot of $(2J+1)$ vs. $J$ on the exponential plots. Compute the relative distributions of populations among rotational levels of the ground vibrational state for the three molecules at the two temperatures. At what value of $J$ does maximum population occur in all cases?

10. Compute for $v = 0$ the value of $J$ for which maximum population occurs at 300°K, 1000°K for both the even- and odd-numbered rotational levels of $H_2$, $D_2$, $N^{15}N^{15}$.

|  | $H_2$ | $D_2$ | $N^{15}N^{15}$ |
|---|---|---|---|
| $B_e$, cm$^{-1}$ | 60.81 | 30.43 | 1.87 |
| $\alpha_e$, cm$^{-1}$ | 2.99 | 1.05 | 0.017 |

11. Besides the $^3\Sigma_g^-$ ground state of $O_2$, there are two other low-lying electronic states, $^1\Delta_g$ and $^1\Sigma_g^+$, for which $T_e = 7918$ and 13,195 cm$^{-1}$, respectively. Compute the relative populations of the three states at 1000°K.

# SUGGESTIONS FOR FURTHER READING

This is not intended to be an exhaustive list. These books are written at a variety of levels and for a variety of purposes. We make no attempt to differentiate them, but list them in alphabetical order by authors.

B. N. BAK, *Elementary Introduction to Molecular Spectra*. New York: Interscience, 1954.

G. M. BARROW, *The Structure of Molecules*. New York: Benjamin, 1963.

G. M. BARROW, *Introduction to Molecular Spectroscopy*. New York: McGraw-Hill, 1962.

A. C. CANDLER, *Atomic Spectra and the Vector Model*, 2nd ed. London: Hilger and Watts, 1964.

C. A. COULSON, *Valence*, 2nd ed. New York: Oxford University Press, 1963.

F. DANIELS and R. ALBERTY, *Physical Chemistry*, 3rd ed., Section III. New York: Wiley, 1966.

D. F. EGGERS, JR., N. W. GREGORY, G. D. HALSEY, JR., and B. S. RABINOVITCH, *Physical Chemistry*, Chapters 1–4, 16. New York: Wiley, 1964.

A. G. GAYDON, *Dissociation Energies and Spectra of Diatomic Molecules*, 2nd ed. London: Chapman and Hall, 1953.

W. GORDY, W. V. SMITH, and R. F. TRAMBARULO, *Microwave Spectroscopy*. New York: Wiley, 1953.

G. HERZBERG, *Atomic Spectra and Atomic Structure*. New York: Dover, 1944.

G. HERZBERG, *Molecular Spectra and Molecular Structure*. Princeton, N.J.: Van Nostrand.

Vol. I: *Spectra of Diatomic Molecules*, 2nd ed., 1950.

Vol. II: *Infrared and Raman Spectra of Polyatomic Molecules*, 1945.

Vol. III: *Electronic Spectra and Electronic Structure of Polyatomic Molecules*, 1966.

R. M. HOCHSTRASSER, *Molecular Aspects of Symmetry*. New York: Benjamin, 1966.

W. JEVONS, *Report on Band Spectra of Diatomic Molecules*. London: Cambridge University Press, 1932.

W. KAUZMANN, *Quantum Chemistry*. New York: Academic Press, 1957.

G. W. KING, *Spectroscopy and Molecular Structure*. New York: Holt, Rinehart, and Winston, 1964.

J. W. Linnett, *The Electronic Structure of Molecules. A New Approach.* London: Methuen, 1964.

J. W. Linnett, *Wave Mechanics and Valency.* New York: Wiley, 1960.

W. J. Moore, *Physical Chemistry,* 3rd ed., Chapter 12–15. Englewood Cliffs, N.J.: Prentice-Hall, 1962.

L. C. Pauling and E. B. Wilson, Jr., *Introduction to Quantum Mechanics.* New York: McGraw-Hill, 1935.

R. W. B. Pearse and A. G. Gaydon, *The Identification of Molecular Spectra,* 3rd ed. London: Chapman and Hall, 1963.

C. Sandorfy, *Electronic Spectra and Quantum Chemistry.* Englewood Cliffs, N.J.: Prentice-Hall, 1964.

R. A. Sawyer, *Experimental Spectroscopy,* 2nd ed. Englewood Cliffs, N.J.: Prentice-Hall, 1951.

J. C. Slater, *Quantum Theory of Atomic Structure,* Vols. 1 and 2. New York: McGraw-Hill, 1960.

J. C. Slater, *Quantum Theory of Molecules and Solids,* Vol. 1: *Electronic Structure of Molecules.* New York: McGraw-Hill, 1962.

# ANSWERS TO SELECTED PROBLEMS

**Chapter 1**

1. (a) $1.23$ Å     (b) $2.72 \times 10^{-36}$ cm
3. $5.52 \times 10^{-33}$ gm
4. $7.16 \times 10^{-12}$ erg/molecule, $4.46$ eV, $1.08 \times 10^{15}$ sec$^{-1}$, $3.6 \times 10^{4}$ cm$^{-1}$
5. $5.45 \times 10^{-3}$ kcal/mole, $2.36 \times 10^{-4}$ eV, $5.73 \times 10^{10}$ sec$^{-1}$, $5.73 \times 10^{4}$ Mc/sec, $3.78 \times 10^{-16}$ erg/molecule
6. $3.60 \times 10^{2}$ kcal/mole, $2.50 \times 10^{-11}$ erg/molecule, $1.26 \times 10^{5}$ cm$^{-1}$, $3.77 \times 10^{15}$ sec$^{-1}$

**Chapter 2**

1. $5.76 \times 10^{-24}$, $11.63 \times 10^{-24}$, $1.62 \times 10^{-24}$ gm
2. $4.43 \times 10^{-40}$ g-cm$^{2}$, $1.66$ Å, $3.00 \times 10^{-13}$ erg/molecule
3. $1.59 \times 10^{11}$, $1.20 \times 10^{12}$ rev/sec
4. $3.68 \times 10^{13}$ rad/sec, $5.85 \times 10^{12}$ rev/sec
5. $2.68 \times 10^{-40}$ g-cm$^{2}$, $1.28$ Å
6. (a) $0.970$ Å                    (b) $5.77 \times 10^{-27}$ g-cm$^{2}$ — sec$^{-1}$
   (c) $3.90 \times 10^{13}$ rad/sec          (d) $227$ cm$^{-1}$, $4.50 \times 10^{-14}$ erg/molecule
8. (a) Mass effects are negligible compared to electronic effects in the determination of $r_e$.
   (b) $B_v$ is $0.15\%$ smaller for HCl$^{37}$ than for HCl$^{35}$, on the basis of our assumptions.
9. $B_v$ is decreased by a factor of 2.

**Chapter 3**

1. $\nu_{\text{OD}} = 7.983 \times 10^{13}$, $\nu_{\text{O18H}} = 1.095 \times 10^{14}$ sec$^{-1}$
2. $\omega_e = 2091$ cm$^{-1}$, $6.27 \times 10^{13}$ sec$^{-1}$, no
3. For H$_2$, HD, and D$_2$, respectively:

   approximately:   6.28,   5.45,   4.46 kcal/mole
        exactly:   6.20,   5.39,   4.41 kcal/mole

4. $41.16$ cm$^{-1}$
5. $\omega_e = 2170.2$ cm$^{-1}$, $\omega_e x_e = 13.5$ cm$^{-1}$, $k = 1.90 \times 10^{6}$ dynes/cm, $\nu = 6.51 \times 10^{13}$ vib/sec
6. $P(2)$, $P(1)$, $R(0)$, and $R(1)$: 1989.68, 2000.34, 2021.66, 2032.32 cm$^{-1}$, respectively

146

7. $B = 10.6$ cm$^{-1}$, $r = 1.27$ Å, $\omega_e = 2{,}991.0$ cm$^{-1}$, $k = 5.14 \times 10^5$ dynes/cm
8. $B = 1.93$ cm$^{-1}$, $r = 1.13$ Å, $\omega_e = 2170.21$ cm$^{-1}$, $k = 1.90 \times 10^6$ dynes/cm
9. For $v = 0$: $0.052$ Å, $4.3\%$; for $v = 15$: $0.29$ Å, $24\%$
10. For $v = 0$: $0.012$ Å, $17\%$; for $v = 15$: $0.686$ Å, $92\%$
11. $B_1 = 8.134$, $B_0 = 8.360$, $\Delta_2 F(8') = 276.56$, $\Delta_2 F(3'') = 117.04$ cm$^{-1}$

## Chapter 4

1. $2234$ Å, $43.6$ kcal/mole
2. (a) $35.53$      (b) $14.10$ kcal/mole
3. $49{,}757$ cm$^{-1}$, $2010$ Å
4. $65{,}074.80$ cm$^{-1}$
5. $787.16$ cm$^{-1}$
10. $\omega_e' = 800$, $\omega_e x_e' = 20$, $\omega_e'' = 1500$, $\omega_e x_e'' = 10$, $T_e = 30{,}000$ cm$^{-1}$
11. $\omega_e' = 1000$, $\omega_e x_e' = 16$, $\omega_e'' = 1600$, $\omega_e x_e'' = 12$, $T_e = 25{,}000$ cm$^{-1}$
12. $T_e = 77$, $612$; $\bar{\nu}_{00} = 87$, $239$ cm$^{-1}$ for $5' \leftarrow 0''$ of DCl$^{35}$.
13. $T_e = 50{,}210$, $\bar{\nu}_{00} = 35{,}848$ for $0' \rightarrow 6''$ band of N$^{14}$N$^{15}$.
14. $5$–$4$: $63{,}445$; $4$–$3$: $64{,}145$; $3$–$2$: $64{,}838$; $2$–$1$: $65{,}523$; $1$–$0$: $66{,}202$ cm$^{-1}$
15. $B_3' = 15.839$, $B_0'' = 59.313$, $\bar{\nu}_{00} = 94{,}026.89$ cm$^{-1}$
16. $14.646$; $59.313$; $95{,}224.35$ cm$^{-1}$
17. $20.016$, $1.193$ cm$^{-1}$, $1.293$ Å
18. $B_0' = 0.156$, $B_0'' = 0.243$, $\bar{\nu}_{00} = 18{,}147.40$ cm$^{-1}$

## Chapter 5

1. $117.2$ kcal/mole
2. $D_e' = 7{,}850$; $D_e'' = 41{,}780$ cm$^{-1}$
3. $D_e' = 2{,}860$; $D_0' = 2{,}740$; $D_e'' = 20{,}290$; $D_0'' = 20{,}010$ cm$^{-1}$
4. $D_0 = 86.64$, $\Delta H^\circ_{\text{diss}} = 87.54$ kcal/mole
5. $\Delta H^\circ = 68.6$, $D_0 = 67.7$ kcal/mole
6. (a) $n_0 : n_1 : n_2 : n_3$ is $1.00 : 0.36 : 0.13 : 0.05$.
   (b) $214$ cm$^{-1}$ ($107$ cm$^{-1}$ in excess of zero-point energy)
   (c) $\Delta H^\circ$ is lowered by $53.5$ cm$^{-1}$ because of I$_2$ vibrational energy.
7. (a) KE: $14.9$ kcal/(mole S$_2$) greater, when the S$_2$ is dissociated.
   (b) $\Delta H^\circ_{\text{diss}} = 104.8$ kcal/mole
   (c) $D_0 = 99.1$ kcal/mole
8. (a) $D_0 = 71.5$ kcal/mole

## Chapter 6

1. $n$, $l$, $m_l$, $m_s$
2. H $1s^1$, $^2$S; He $1s^2$, $^1$S; B $1s^2 2s^2 2p^1$, $^2$P; N $^4$S; 0 $1s^2 2s^2 2p^4$, $^3$P
4. $\uparrow\uparrow$, $\uparrow\downarrow$, $\downarrow\downarrow$
5. (a) 3 (a triplet state)
6. sextet state
7. $^3$D, $^3$P, $^3$S, $^1$D, $^1$P, $^1$S
8. $^3$P $<$ $^1$D $<$ $^1$S

10. ss, $^1$S, $^3$S; sd, $^1$D, $^3$D

11. p and p$^5$, $^2$P; d$^2$ and d$^8$, $^3$F, $^3$P, $^1$G, $^1$D, $^1$S. (G and H terms come after S, P, D, F).

## Chapter 7

2. $^1\Delta$, $^1\Pi$, $^1\Sigma$, $^3\Delta$, $^3\Pi$, $^3\Sigma$, $^5\Delta$, $^5\Pi$, $^5\Sigma$

3. (a) $^1\Sigma$, $^1\Pi$    (b) $^3\Sigma$, $^3\Pi$

5. $^3\Delta_3$, $^3\Delta_2$, $^3\Delta_1$

6. (a)$^2\Pi_{3/2}$, $^2\Pi_{1/2}$

7. $O_2KK(z\sigma_g)^2(y\sigma_u)^2(x\sigma_g)^2(w\pi_u)^4(v\pi_g)^2$, $^3\Sigma_g$ (strictly, $^3\Sigma_g^-$; see the next chapter)

8. $B_2$ $^3\Sigma$; others $^1\Sigma$, $N_2 > C_2 \simeq O_2 > B_2 \simeq F_2 > Li_2 \gg Ne_2$.

## Chapter 8

4. $^1\Pi$

5. $B_0 = 0.7520$, $B_1 = 0.7480$ cm$^{-1}$, $^1\Delta$, heteronuclear

7. $\Delta_1 F(8') = 108.58$; $\Delta_1 F(4'') = 64.53$ cm$^{-1}$; $^1\Pi - ^1\Pi$

## Chapter 9

1. (a) $+ \leftrightarrow\!\!\!/ -$    (b) $\Delta S = 0$ only    (c) $\Delta S = 0$ only; $\Delta\Lambda = 0, \pm 1$
   (d) $u \leftrightarrow\!\!\!/ u$    (e) $\Delta\Omega = 0$ only

4. $P(2), Q(1), R(0)$

5. (b)

(f)

9. $J = 1, \mathcal{E} = 0.15; J = 4, \mathcal{E} = 0.41$ cm$^{-1}$

## Chapter 10

5. For $^1\Sigma_g^+$, the ratio of odd-numbered to even-numbered rotational level populations is $21:28$, $21:15$ for $B_2$ and $O^{17}O^{17}$, respectively.

9. For HCl at 300°K, the relative populations are $1:2.72:3.70:3.85:3.37:2.46$ for $J = 0, 1, 2, 3, 4, 5$, respectively.

# Principal Symbols

Greek symbols are listed according to the first letter of their English spelling. Upper states are indicated by primes (') on the appropriate symbols, lower states by double primes ("). An absorption process is indicated by the symbol ←, an emission process by →.

| Symbol | Meaning | Page on which first used or defined |
|---|---|---|
| $\alpha_e$ | Rotational constant | 58 |
| $\alpha$ | Electron with spin $\frac{1}{2}\hbar$ | 134 |
| Å | Angstrom unit | 4 |
| $a$ | Antisymmetric | 123 |
| $a$ | Parabolic constant for band spectra | 36 |
| $A$ | Rotational constant for a symmetric top | 109 |
| $A$ | Einstein coefficient of spontaneous emission | 125 |
| $A$ | Splitting constant for multiplet states | 114 |
| $A$-axis | Axis through two nuclei | 107 |
| $A_{\text{exc}}$ | Atomic electronic excitation energy | 60 |
| a.o. | Atomic orbital | 71 |
| $\beta$ | Electron with spin $-\frac{1}{2}\hbar$ | 134 |
| $\beta$ | Morse potential energy constant | 44 |
| $\beta$ | Spin of deuteron | 139 |
| $b$ | Parabolic constant for band spectra | 36 |
| $B$ | Rotational constant | 33, 107 |
| $B$-axis | Axis at right angles to internuclear axis | 107 |
| $B_M$ | Bohr magneton | 76 |
| $B_v$ | Rotational constant. Subscript indicates vibrational quantum number | 22 |
| $c$ | Parabolic constant for band spectra | 36 |
| $c$ | Velocity of light | 2 |
| $C$ | Energy required to observe a continuous spectrum or continuum | 60 |
| $\Delta$ | Spectroscopic term for molecule with $\Lambda = 2$ | 94 |
| $\Delta\lambda$ | Difference in wavelength | 8 |
| $\Delta\theta$ | Difference in angle | 8 |

149

| Symbol | Meaning | Page on which first used or defined |
|--------|---------|------------|
| $\Delta G$ | Spacing between adjacent vibrational levels | 67 |
| $\Delta H°$ | Standard heat of reaction, the heat of dissociation in the case of a dissociation reaction | 63 |
| $\Delta p$ | Uncertainty in momentum | 2 |
| $\Delta x$ | Uncertainty in position | 2 |
| D | Spectroscopic term for atom with $l = 2$ | 85 |
| $D_e$ | Bond-dissociation energy, measured from minimum of potential-energy well | 41 |
| $D_0$ | Bond-dissociation energy measured from *zeroth* vibrational level | 59 |
| d-orbital | Atomic orbital occupied by an electron with $l = 2$ | 74 |
| $d\theta/d\lambda$ | Angular dispersion | 8 |
| $dx/d\lambda$ | Linear dispersion | 8 |
| $e$ | Charge on an electron | 4 |
| $E$ | Energy | 2 |
| $F$ | Restoring force on a harmonic oscillator | 26 |
| $F(J)$ | Rotational term or energy in $cm^{-1}$ | 21 |
| $G(v)$ | Vibrational term or energy in $cm^{-1}$ | 29 |
| $g_i$ | Statistical weight factor | 64 |
| $h$ | Planck's constant | 2 |
| $\hbar$ | Planck's constant divided by $2\pi$ | 22 |
| $i$ | Superscript to indicate isotopic species | 54 |
| $I$ | Moment of inertia | 20 |
| $I$ | Nuclear spin quantum number | 136 |
| $I_A$ | Moment of inertia about the $A$-axis | 108 |
| $I_B$ | Moment of inertia about the $B$-axis | 108 |
| $J$ | Rotational quantum number | 21 |
| $k$ | Harmonic force constant | 26 |
| $K$ | Chemical equilibrium constant | 63 |
| $\lambda$ | Molecular quantum number, the value of which is proportional to the orbital angular momentum of a single electron | 97 |
| $\lambda$ | Wavelength | 4 |
| $\Lambda$ | Molecular quantum number, the value of which is proportional to the total orbital angular momentum of the electrons | 93 |
| $\mathbf{\Lambda}$ | Vector corresponding to $\Lambda$ | 93 |
| $l$ | Atomic quantum number, the value of which is proportional to the orbital angular momentum of a single electron | 71 |
| $\mathbf{l}$ | Vector corresponding to $l$ | 80 |

| Symbol | Meaning | Page on which first used or defined |
|---|---|---|
| $L$ | Quantum number, the value of which is proportional to total angular momentum of all electrons | 80 |
| $\mathbf{L}$ | Vector corresponding to $L$ | 80 |
| LCAO-MO | Linear combination of atomic orbitals to yield molecular orbitals | 96 96 |
| $\mu$ | Micron | 4 |
| $\mu$ | Reduced mass | 21 |
| $m$ | Mass | 2 |
| $m$ | Quantum number for Fortrat parabola | 35 |
| $M$ | Angular momentum | 21 |
| $m_e$ | Mass of an electron | 76 |
| $m_l$ | Magnetic quantum number for an electron | 71 |
| $M_L$ | Molecular quantum number, the absolute value of which is proportional to the total angular momentum of the electrons | 93 |
| $m\mu$ | Millimicron | 4 |
| $M(\phi)$ | Wave function dependent on angle $\phi$ | 73 |
| $M_{m_l}(\phi)$ | See $M(\phi)$ | |
| $m_s$ | Spin quantum number of an electron, obtained by the projection of $\mathbf{s}$ on the axis in the direction of the magnetic field | 77 |
| $\bar{\nu}_{00}$ | Null gap, zero line, band origin | 31, 33 |
| $n$ | Principal quantum number | 71 |
| $n_i$ | Number of molecules in the $i$th energy level | 64 |
| $N$ | Avogadro's number | 4 |
| $N$ | Normalization factor | 73 |
| $\mathbf{N}$ | Vector representing angular momentum of nuclear rotation for a symmetric-top molecule | 108 |
| $N_{nlm_l}$ | Normalization factor | 73 |
| $\omega$ | Angular velocity | 21 |
| $\omega_e$ | Harmonic vibrational frequency constant | 29 |
| $\omega_e x_e$ | Anharmonic vibrational frequency constant | 30 |
| $\Omega$ | Quantum number, the magnitude of which is proportional to total angular momentum of a Hund's case-(a) molecule | 94 |
| $\mathbf{\Omega}$ | Vector corresponding to $\Omega$ | 94 |
| $\Pi$ | Spectroscopic term for molecule with $\Lambda = 2$ | 94 |
| $\psi$ | Wave equation | 21, 49, 72 |
| P | Spectroscopic term for atom with $L = 1$ | 85 |
| $P(J)$ | Energy of a $P$-branch transition expressed in terms of the quantum number $J$ | 34 |

| Symbol | Meaning | Page on which first used or defined |
|---|---|---|
| $P(m)$ | Energy of a $P$-branch transition expressed in terms of the quantum number $m$ | 36 |
| $P_{lm_l}(\theta)$ | Wave function dependent on angle $\theta$ | 73 |
| p-orbital | Atomic orbital occupied by an electron with $l = 1$ | 72 |
| $Q(J)$ | Energy of a $Q$-branch transition expressed in terms of the quantum number $J$ | 111 |
| $\rho$ | Square root of the ratio of the reduced masses of two isotopic molecules | 54 |
| $r_e$ | Equilibrium internuclear distance | 41 |
| $r_v$ | Mean internuclear distance when the vibrational quantum number is equal to $v$ | 49 |
| $R(J)$ | Energy of a $R$-branch transition expressed in terms of the quantum number $J$ | 33 |
| $R(m)$ | Energy of an R-branch transition expressed in terms of the quantum number $m$ | 36 |
| $R_{nl}(r)$ | Wave equation dependent on $r$, the distance from nucleus to electron | 73 |
| $\Sigma$ | Spectroscopic term for molecule with $\Lambda = 0$ | 94 |
| $\Sigma$ | Quantum number, the value of which is given by the allowed projections of $\mathbf{S}$ on the internuclear axis | 94 |
| $\mathbf{\Sigma}$ | Vector corresponding to $\Sigma$ | 94 |
| $s$ | Electron spin quantum number | 77 |
| $\mathbf{s}$ | Vector corresponding to $s$ | 77 |
| s-orbital | Atomic orbital occupied by an electron with $l = 0$ | 72 |
| $S$ | Spectroscopic term for atom with $L = 0$ | 85 |
| $S$ | Total electron spin quantum number | 80 |
| $\mathbf{S}$ | Vector corresponding to $S$ | 80 |
| $\tau$ | Period of one vibration | 27 |
| $T$ | Energy of upper-or lower-state levels in $\text{cm}^{-1}$ | 33 |
| $T$ | Total spin of nuclei | 137 |
| $T_e$ | Energy difference in $\text{cm}^{-1}$ between the minima in two electronic potential-energy wells | 45 |
| $T(P)$ | Energy of levels in $\text{cm}^{-1}$ associated with $P$-branch transitions | 33 |
| $T(R)$ | Energy of levels in $\text{cm}^{-1}$ associated with $R$-branch transitions | 33 |
| $v$ | Velocity | 2 |
| $v$ | Vibrational quantum number | 29 |
| $V$ | Potential energy | 26 |
| $V$ | Voltage | 4 |

# Author Index

# Subject Index

Absorption spectra, 6, 8
  continuous, 47, 48
  electronic, 46
    of $S_2$, 12
  notation to indicate, 33
  rotational, 23
    of CO, 24
    of HCl, 24
    of SCSe, 24
  vibration-rotation, 26, 30, 33
    of HBr, 15
    of CO, 32
    of NO, 113, 131
$A$-axis, principal axis, 107, 108
Abundance of isotopes 5, 160
AlH, 132, 133
Allowed transitions, 45, 46; see also
    Selection rules
$Al_2O_3$, 16
Alternate weak or missing lines, for
    homonuclear molecules, 127, 129,
    131, 138
Amplifier, 6
Amplitude of vibration, 27, 30
Angstrom units, 4
Angular dispersion, 8, 11
Angular momentum, 21, 77, 108
  of electrons, 74, 75, 77
  of vectors, 74–94, 114, 115
Angular velocity, 21
Anharmonic effects, 55, 67, 68
Anharmonic vibration, 30, 55
Anomalous Zeeman effect, 86
Antenna, 15
Antibonding orbitals, 96, 103
Antiparallel spins; see Spins
Assignment of $J$ or $m$ values 52
Associated Laguerre polynomials, 71, 73
Associated Legendre polynomials, 71, 73
Asymptote of potential-energy curve, 41,
    42
Atom combinations, 41, 95
Atomic clocks, 17
Atomic orbitals 71, 72
Atomic weights, 5, 160
Aufbau principle; see Building-up
    principle

Average bond energies, 66
Avogadro's number, 4, 64
Azimuthal quantum number; see Orbital
    quantum number

$B$-axis, 107, 108
$B_2$-molecule, ground state of, 100
Band heads, 50, 51, 52, 54, 132
Band origin, 55; see also Null gap
Band progressions, 52, 54, 60
Bands, observed, 12, 13, 15, 23, 24, 32,
    51, 113, 132
  schematic, 30, 111
Band spectra; see Electronic band spectra,
    Vibration-rotation spectra
Barometric pressure formula, 64
Birge-Sponer method of obtaining bond-
    dissociation energies, 66, 68
Blackbody radiator, 1, 15
Bohr magneton, 77
Boltzmann:
  constant, 64
  distribution function, 64, 138, 141
  factor; see Boltzmann distribution
    function
Bond-dissociation energies, 41, 44, 45, 48,
    59
Bonding orbitals, 96, 103
Born-Oppenheimer approximation, 43
Bose-Einstein statistics, 140
Bosons, 140
$Br_2$, 55
Branches of a band (see $P$-, $Q$- and
    $R$-branches)
Building-up (aufbau) principle, 79

$C_2$-molecule, ground state of, 100
$CH_4$, 66
$Cm^{-1}$, 4, 5, 159
Cal, 4, 5, 159
Camera lens, 8
Cat's whisker, 15
Centrifugal distortion, 23
Chemical bond, 41, 45
$Cl_2$, 55
Classical or Newtonian mechanics, 21, 26,
    46

ABCD-698

**Table 1**

FUNDAMENTAL CONSTANTS

| | | | |
|---|---|---|---|
| $c$ | velocity of light | = | $3.000 \times 10^{10}$ cm/sec |
| $h$ | Planck's constant | = | $6.623 \times 10^{-27}$ erg-sec |
| $N$ | Avogadro's number | = | $6.023 \times 10^{23}$ |
| $e$ | electron charge | = | $1.602 \times 10^{-19}$ coulombs |
| $m$ | electron mass | = | $9.106 \times 10^{-28}$ g |
| $R$ | gas constant | = | $8.315 \times 10^{7}$ erg/deg-mole |
| | | = | $1.987$ cal/deg-mole |
| | | = | $0.08205$ l-atm/deg-mole |

**Table 2**

ENERGY CONVERSION FACTORS

| | $cm^{-1}$ | $sec^{-1}$ | erg/particle | cal/$N$ particles | eV |
|---|---|---|---|---|---|
| 1 $cm^{-1}$ = | 1 | $3.000 \times 10^{10}$ | $1.986 \times 10^{-16}$ | 2.858 | $1.239 \times 10^{-4}$ |
| 1 $sec^{-1}$ = | $3.333 \times 10^{-11}$ | 1 | $6.618 \times 10^{-7}$ | $9.528 \times 10^{-11}$ | $4.131 \times 10^{-15}$ |
| 1 erg/particle = | $5.036 \times 10^{15}$ | $1.510 \times 10^{6}$ | 1 | $1.440 \times 10^{16}$ | $6.242 \times 10^{11}$ |
| 1 cal/$N$ particles = | 0.3498 | $1.050 \times 10^{10}$ | $6.946 \times 10^{-17}$ | 1 | $4.336 \times 10^{-5}$ |
| 1 eV = | 8068 | $2.421 \times 10^{14}$ | $1.602 \times 10^{-12}$ | 23,060 | 1 |

**Table 3**

ATOMIC WEIGHTS* TO FOUR SIGNIFICANT FIGURES, AND RELATIVE ABUNDANCE† OF SOME ISOTOPES

| Isotope | Atomic weight | Approximate % natural abundance |
|---------|---------------|----------------------------------|
| $H^1$ | 1.009 | 99.98 |
| $H^2(D)$ | 2.014 | 0.016 |
| $He^4$ | 4.002 | 100 |
| $Li^7$ | 7.016 | 92.6 |
| $C^{12}$ | 12 exactly | 98.89 |
| $C^{13}$ | 13.00 | 1.11 |
| $N^{14}$ | 14.00 | 99.64 |
| $N^{15}$ | 15.00 | 0.36 |
| $O^{16}$ | 15.995 | 99.76 |
| $O^{18}$ | 18.00 | 0.20 |
| $F^{19}$ | 19.00 | 100 |
| $Al^{27}$ | 26.98 | 100 |
| $S^{32}$ | 31.97 | 95.0 |
| $S^{34}$ | 33.97 | 4.2 |
| $Cl^{35}$ | 34.97 | 75.4 |
| $Cl^{37}$ | 36.97 | 24.6 |
| $Br^{79}$ | 78.92 | 50.6 |
| $Br^{81}$ | 80.92 | 49.4 |
| $I^{127}$ | 126.9 | 100 |

* The new atomic weight scale, accepted by both chemists and physicists, is based on the weight of $6.023 \times 10^{23}$ atoms of $C^{12} = 12$ gm exactly. It differs by about 4 parts per $10^6$ from the old chemists' scale. In spectroscopic work, atomic weights for individual isotopes, and not mean atomic weights for elements, must be used.

† Small variations can occur in natural isotope abundances, which may affect the mean atomic weight of elements in the third decimal place.

2514   79